D1601985

HOW TO RUN A

COMMUNITY RECYCLING CENTER

by Anna L. Engelhardt [1]

James R. Thompson, Governor
State of Illinois

Michael B. Witte, Director
Illinois Department of Energy and
Natural Resources

WITHDRAW

**Books for Business
New York-Hong Kong**

COLORADO COLLEGE LIBRARY
COLORADO SPRINGS
COLORADO

How to Run a Community Recycling Center

by
Anna L. Engelhardt

ISBN: 0-89499-152-3

Copyright © 2002 by Books for Business

Reprinted from the 1982 edition

Books for Business
New York - Hong Kong
http://www.BusinessBooksInternational.com

All rights reserved, including the right to reproduce
this book, or portions thereof, in any form.

Contents

TD
7945
E537X
2002

List of Tables

(By Section)

Acknowledgments

Sincere thanks to the many Illinois
recyclers who contributed to the
completion of this project, and
especially to:

George Brabec

Greg Lindsey

Ronald Seifert

Hans-Dieter Drehsler

Community Renewal Society

Niles Township High Schools
Environmental Resource Center

Illinois Association
of Recycling Centers

* NATIONS THAT DEPEND ON LIMITED NATURAL RESOURCES * CAN'T AFFORD TO THROW THEM AWAY

How To Run A Community Recycling Center

A RESOURCE GUIDE TO LOW TECHNOLOGY RECYCLING IN ILLINOIS

INTRODUCTION

It's a steamy, smelly mess. It's a conglomeration of the way we live. Trash. Garbage. Household refuse. Municipal solid waste. Whatever you call it -- Americans certainly produce plenty of it -- table scraps, pop cans, TV dinner trays, newspapers, pickle jars -- the list of things that we throw away is almost endless. It's our garbage, and it can be a pain in the neck (and the pocketbook) from the first "Will you take out the garbage, dear?" to the tax drain to the threat of a sanitary landfill moving in next door.

Most Americans toss their garbage into the trash can and never wonder what happens next. But it will be back. Every last bit of garbage will haunt us unless we consider innovative ways of handling it.

Part of the solution is available or could be available to all of us right in our own communities -- RECYCLING -- sending a material back for reuse into the process by which it was first formed. And because you are reading this book, you are already aware and concerned about your community's waste disposal problem. The next step is to do something about it.

1

This guide is directed mainly to environmental clubs and organizations, scouts, church groups, schools, service clubs, and individuals who wish to earn some extra cash while performing a vital community service.

In the pages of this guide, you will find an array of operational options for recycling centers, techniques for marketing and handling recyclables, and suggestions for making your project competitive and successful. Recycling projects can be and have been successful. You too can help rid a portion of our society of its throwaway mentality if you are determined to implement different recycling options as needs and opportunities arise.

There is no one model way of running a recycling project. With this book, we hope to give you solid information about the most common methods used by community-based recycling organizations in Illinois, advise you of possible pitfalls, and suggest additional resources for aid in developing your program. Most of all, we want to be encouraging -- to let you know that there is no better day than today to begin your project. Recycling may have become popular in the early 70's, but the positive impacts of recycling have never been more important.

The Problem

Think about those quick trips most of us occasionally make to the grocery store. You might buy a newspaper, a foil-lined can of frozen orange juice, a couple of apples, a plastic carton of yogurt, a jar of jelly, a can of tuna, and a chicken pot pie. You read the newspaper, drink the juice, and eat the food. Everything that is left over you toss in the trash can.

If we only had to dispose of an occasional small bag of trash, we wouldn't have much of a waste crisis on our hands. But think about the number of trips you actually make to the store and the amount of trash you have to dispose of each week. You may want to use the trash profile on the next page to see how much waste you actually create in your home in one week.[1]

Once you have added up all your household refuse, think about all the other places you create trash -- at work or school, at the roller rink, at the movies, on vacation, in the laundromat, etc. Multiply it by the 11.4 million people who live in Illinois, add the amount of waste industry makes before the products ever get to you, and you can see we are talking about alot of waste. What happens to all of this garbage?

Y O U R   T R A S H   P R O F I L E[2]

IS EVERYTHING YOU'RE THROWING AWAY REALLY GARBAGE?

Day	News-Paper LBS.	Cans & Metal LBS.	Other Paper LBS.	Plastic LBS.	Glass LBS.	Food Refuse* LBS.	Other
SUN.							
MON.							
TUE.							
WED.							
THU.							
FRI.							
SAT.							
TOTAL							

* Not Oil and Meat

ADD ALL TOTALS FOR THE GRAND TOTAL _____

_____ x 52 WEEKS = _____
Grand Total   Lbs. Per Year
                                     (estimated)

4

A *DUMP* is a land site where refuse is disposed of in such a way that it often harms the environment. Dumping garbage indiscriminately can lead to fires and gas explosions, rats and insect pests, blowing litter and odor. Leachate, the concentrated liquid that forms when water filters through waste, can be a very real and dangerous problem. Once leachate has contaminated groundwater, it is difficult and expensive to clean up.

Federal legislation requires that all dumps in our nation be phased out within five years, and that means getting rid of solid waste will be more expensive. But if our trash doesn't go to a dump, where does it go?

SANITARY LANDFILLS are the primary method of disposal in Illinois. At these sites, garbage is compacted and covered frequently with soil or other approved cover material to prevent or minimize burning and odor, pests, and blowing litter. Designed to control leachate and thereby avoid water pollution, sanitary landfills are certainly positive alternatives to dumps. But there are some very real drawbacks to putting all of our discards into landfills.

Burying our garbage means many valuable resources such as paper, glass, metal, and organic matter, are lost forever. Our landfill sites are rapidly being filled and many will run out of room for our garbage within the next five to ten years. As long as we are making trash, new sites will have to be found. But finding new sites is difficult. Only sites which meet specific requirements will do.

Once appropriate land is found, the most difficult part of landfill siting is getting public support for the site. No matter how much garbage we produce ourselves, we want it disposed of as far away from us as possible. Given all the difficulties related to sanitary landfills, the goal seems clear: we want to save landfill space for the "real" garbage (things which cannot be reused or recycled) and rescue everything else. How do we go about saving things from reaching the landfill?

The Solution

All across the country, citizens groups are becoming involved in handling and recovering materials from solid waste. For many, this activity means separating glass, metals, and paper. _SOURCE SEPARATION_ means keeping the things which can be reused or recycled separate from our garbage. It is the first step in the recycling process and can be practiced in homes, offices, restaurants, schools, and any other place where we produce garbage. If properly prepared, your old newspaper, glass jelly jar, tuna fish can, aluminum pie tin, and grocery sack could be collected and taken to a depot. The depot in turn sells the materials to manufacturers for reuse.

Today recycling is taking on a new importance as a means of alleviating impending shortages and reducing the solid waste stream. But recycling is not new.

* One of the earliest groups to recognize the need
  for conservation was the Salvation Army. Founded
  in 1865 by William Booth in London, England, it
  has been in the business of collecting, separating, and recycling waste for over 100 years.

* During the Great Depression, President Franklin
  D. Roosevelt called upon Americans to conserve
  and recycle in the face of severe shortages
  and high prices.

* Another grassroots conservation movement emerged
  in the 1940's, when during World War II, thousands of tons of materials were recycled to support the Alleid cause.[3]

Following World War II, Americans fell back into
their former habits of wastefulness and carelessness.
Citizens quickly forgot their wartime practices and
soon reacquired a carefree, "throwaway" spirit that
endured into the 1970's. America was the land of
abundance -- "There will always be more." But in the
1970's, Americans in great number became concerned about
problems of dwindling resources and environmental degrad
ation. People began to ask: "Would it make sense to
recycle our wastes?"

The answer was a resounding "Yes!" And as 1980's
prices for manufacturing products from virgin materials
skyrocket, recycling once again has an urgency akin to
wartime necessity. The opportunities for recycling are
better now than ever -- and so are the rewards.

Beginning a Recycling Project

"This country was founded by people, the frontiersmen and so on who were free to do what they had to do, who took risks, were encouraged to take them and in many instances had to take them whether they were encouraged or not. They won or lost, benefited or died, on the basis of their own internal capability."

The major components of any recycling program are labor, land, and equipment. Labor may be comprised of both voluntary and paid personnel. Thus labor costs depend on the mix of volunteer and paid workers and the amount of manual processing needed for the materials you collect. Some community recycling centers emphasize manual processing so as to provide training and work for the handicapped or unemployed. Land is often donated, sold at nominal cost, or leased to the recycling center. Equipment can also be obtained this way, although at nonprofit centers it is usually purchased secondhand.[4]

How you choose to use the resources of labor, land and equipment will depend on the extend of their availability in your community and the goals you have set for your program. But before you begin, consider the following questions in deciding what sort of project is best suited to the community's needs and your own.

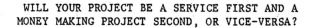

WILL YOUR PROJECT BE A SERVICE FIRST AND A
MONEY MAKING PROJECT SECOND, OR VICE-VERSA?

Community-operated volunteer and charity organizations have been successfully recycling selected materials
for a number of years. A large amount of recycling is
undertaken in the private sector by landfill operators,
secondary fiber dealers, scrap metal dealers, and major
can and paper manufacturing companies. Profit for these
businesses is the bottom line, so in order to maintain
company viability, private recycling is usually limited
to profitable components such as aluminum, newspaper,
and cardboard.

Community recycling projects are usually operated
by nonprofit organizations formed by environmentally
conscientious individuals who see recycling as a means
of alleviating solid waste management problems rather
than as a means of making large profits. Revenues from
the sale of profitable recyclables are often used to
cover the cost of handling less-profitable materials.[5]

If your goal is to raise funds for your organization, you may choose to handle only one or two profitable items. If providing the service of recycling is
your major intent, you may be willing to collect additional materials, some of which might even cost you money
to handle. In any event, it is advisable to begin small
until you see just what the costs might be. Some recycling organizations operate with grant dollars to help
defray expenses, but if your group is not so fortunate,
covering expenses will be essential.

WHAT RECYCLING IS ALREADY GOING ON IN YOUR AREA?

First, check with your local chamber of commerce or
city hall. They will often be able to refer you to
organizations operating ongoing recycling projects in
your community.

Two other resources are invaluable. Obtain a copy
of the *Illinois Directory of Environmental Information*
from the Illinois Department of Energy and Natural Resources, 309 W. Washington, Chicago IL 60606. This free
government publication contains up-to-date listings of
known community recycling programs currently operating
in Illinois. Also contact the *Illinois Association of
Recycling Centers*, P.O. Box 48761, Chicago IL 60648.

10

You may be able to share collection, transportation, or educational projects with existing organizations. Be prepared to plan around these projects to avoid unnecessary competition or duplication of effort. This is especially important in small towns and rural areas. If, for example, the Scouts have an ongoing newspaper collection drive, consider turning your attention to glass, aluminum, or other recyclables; or work with the Scouts to recover newspaper from a neighborhood they don't cover.[6]

WHAT LIMITATIONS DO YOU HAVE THAT WILL DICTATE WHAT SORT OF PROJECT IS BEST?

You want to begin a community recycling center. It's a good idea -- provided you know what it takes and have what it takes. This guide will offer many options for the mechanics of operating your project. If you study it carefully, you will have done some hard work and serious thinking. That's good.

But what about you? Are you the kind of person who can get a business started and make it go? If you are not certain, think about some of these questions as they apply to you personally.

> Are you a self-starter?
> How do you feel about other people?
> Can you lead others?
> Can you take responsibility?
> How good an organizer are you?
> Can you make decisions?
> Can you stick with it? [7]

These reflective questions are recommended by the U.S. Small Business Administration for those about to begin a business. And, although you may view your recycling program as a community service project, it is a business nonetheless.

If you are honest with yourself, you will have found there are some things you still need to know more about. Do all you can for yourself, and don't hesitate to ask for help from people who can tell you what you need to know. Remember, running a business takes guts. You've got to be able to decide what you need and then go after it!

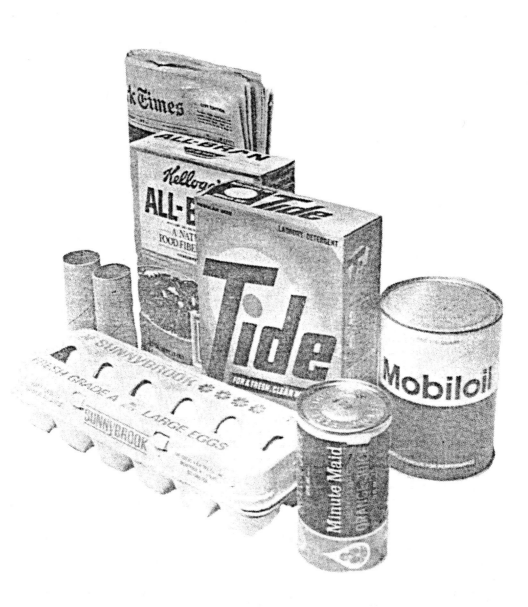

What Materials
Should You Collect?

> *"If you happen to catch hold of an idea, and it begins to move with you, there's very little you can do to kill it. So I don't know that I would worry about bigness or smallness. Correctness of the idea is better."*

When deciding what materials to accept, you should consider availability of manpower, markets and equipment, size of facilities, and what projects already exist. Illinois projects commonly handle glass; tin, bimetal, and aluminum cans; and newspaper products. Other materials such as used crankcase oil are sometimes added to the list of a full-line project.

Visiting different kinds of recycling programs in your area can help you to decide what type of projects to start and what materials to collect. The experience of many now-successful groups suggests that it is easiest to begin by collecting one item such as newspaper or glass expanding to other items as you can.

Don't waste America.

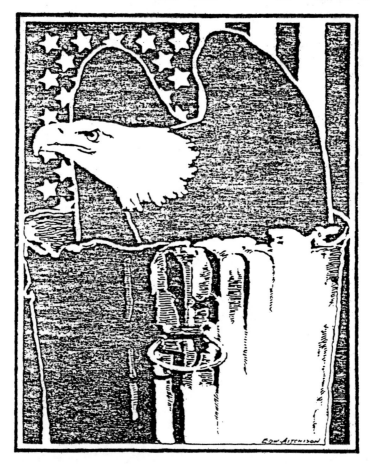

Everytime you throw away a newspaper or a bottle you throw away a piece of America And now, we're staring into the face of a critical shortage of places to bury the things we throw away. And, at the same time, a growing shortage of energy and natural resources'

How can we stop wasting America? We can turn our wastes into resources once again by recycling them, stretching our reserves of virgin natural resources and conserving energy and landfill space.

Recyclable Materials in Your Refuse

Before beginning any recycling program, you should know what is in your garbage so that adequate predictions may be made on what may be collected as recoverable materials. Recommended recyclable materials in this guide have been limited to those that make up a significant portion of the garbage you and your neighbors throw away regularly, are easily collected and sorted, and are marketable at this time.

Aluminum

Aluminum is by far one of the most valuable scrap materials in refuse. Aluminum is the metal of today and its approximate $400 to $600 per ton scrap value (1982) reflects this. Aluminum smelters apparently are eager to reclaim the scrap, and many recycling programs have been instigated by the aluminum companies themselves.

Most of the aluminum in your community's garbage will be in the form of beverage cans. Some is in broken furniture supports, foil, food trays, and other forms. Most recycling centers collect the beverage can portion but leave out the bulkier items. Aluminum companies generally pay between 20 and 30 cents (1982) per pound for clean cans.

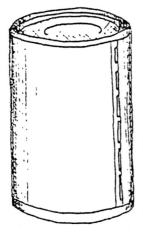

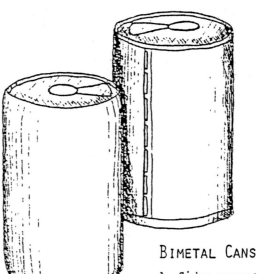

STEEL (TIN) CANS

1. Are magnetic.
2. Have flat tops and bottoms.
3. Have side seam.
4. Have paper labels.

ALUMINUM CANS

1. Are not magnetic.
2. Are lightweight.
3. Have rounded bottoms with shiny surface finish.
4. Have no side seam.
5. Usually pull-top or easy-open.

BIMETAL CANS

1. Sides magnetic; tops non-magnetic.
2. May or may not have side seam.
3. Tops and bottoms often flat; bottom may be rounded with dull surface finish.
4. Usually have pull-top

In order to assure that it is clean, saleable scrap, recyclers must be educated. A major problem is proper identification of "all aluminum" cans. Many cans are deceiving because they have aluminum tops and bottoms but steel barrels. All-aluminum cans are seamless, have rounded shiny bottoms, and cannot be picked up with a magnet.

16

To help save space, cans should be crushed. They should also be empty of all liquids and rinsed to avoid flies being attracted.

If there is a significant amount of aluminum can use in the area, the possibility of recycling aluminum should be considered. Aluminum has a relatively stable market value which has been on the increase. It can be a valuable input to a program. Also remember that it requires 95 percent less energy to process aluminum metal from scrap than from raw resources.

Ferrous Metals

Ferrous metals constitute approximately 8.5 percent of the trash we throw away. About 13 percent of this is in the form of steel cans. Tin coated or bimetal cans are normally the form of steel recovered by community recycling centers. They are relatively uniform, light-weight, easily handled, and may be easily processed for recycling by the consumer in the home. For most recycling projects, the cans must be rinsed free of food particles, have labels removed, ends cut out, and usually must be crushed (simply by stepping on the middle) to reduce their size.

Glass

Glass has changed little in composition throughout the years. The basic raw materials still consist of sand, soda ash, and limestone. Glass scrap, called *CULLET*, is a valuable input in today's glass manufac-turing process. The resale value of cullet is relatively low, approximately $30-$40 per ton (1982), but more stable than many other scrap markets. If markets are reasonably nearby, glass recycling may be a worthwhile addition to your recycling effort.

Cullet is desireable to glass manufacturers because it melts at a lower temperature than do raw materials. It, therefore, requires less heat and energy to process. Consequently, air pollution is reduced and furnace wear in the plant is retarded.

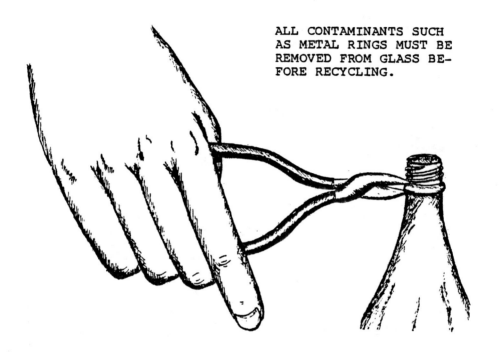

ALL CONTAMINANTS SUCH
AS METAL RINGS MUST BE
REMOVED FROM GLASS BE-
FORE RECYCLING.

Recycling projects should limit their glass collection to container glass only. It is most abundant
and easiest to handle. Cullet collected will most
likely be one of three major colors: flint (clear),
amber (brown), or green. Flint is the most desireable
cullet and becomes worthless if other colors of glass
are mixed with it. Cullet for green or amber production need not be so pure. Some companies may accept
a green/brown mixture, but most prefer all three
separated.

Cullet which can be sold to local glass manufacturing
companies must usually meet the following minimum specifications:

1. Be free of dirt and organic contaminants;

2. Be color sorted according to the individual company's desires; and

3. Be free of metallic contaminants, especially iron or aluminum (remove any metal caps or rings).

Paper

Paper is normally the most important material handled by a community recycling center. In fact, many recycling programs recycle paper only. It is plentiful, easy to separate, easy to handle, and has been successfully recycled from post-consumer waste for decades. In short, it represents a tried and true materials recovery method with established markets. The biggest challenge in this form of recycling is mastering or living with unstable market conditions.

The paper available in your community's waste can be divided into four main categories: office papers, newsprint, corrugated, and mixed. The table on the next page defines these plus other terms common in the business. "Mixed" paper consists of a mixture of any or all of the other categories plus magazines, packaging materials, and any other miscellaneous paper waste.

Americans have been separating and saving their newspaper long before Earth Day, 1970. Girl Scout organizations Boy Scout organizations, schools, and civic and social clubs conducted paper drives. Both the concept and processes are familiar to householders. Studies indicate that the average consumer generates approximately 53 pounds of newspaper per month. Preparation time for the consumer is estimated at only 13 minutes per month, and the only cost required consists of the string or bag to bind the materials.

It is important to note that consumer-level recycling of newsprint and other papers has been found by the U.S. Environmental Protection Agency to be the best method available to date for collection of paper. Even cities entering into elaborate energy recovery facilities are encouraged to recycle paper through consumer recycling programs because the paper will be recycled in its most valuable, uncontaminated form.

Remember that separation requirements may differ according to the specifications of the paper purchaser. Some will accept mixed papers, others only newsprint, and still others office papers only. You must become educated as to the proper separation procedures in order to assure a marketable product.

PAPER STOCK TERMINOLOGY[8]

TERM	DEFINITION
1. Bulk Grades	Grades used in large quantities in paperboard and construction products (3 classifications)
a. News	Consists of old newspapers recovered from residential sources and newspaper publishers
b. Corrugated	Consists of old corrugated boxes recovered from commercial establishments and new clippings from box converting operations
c. Mixed	Covers a wide range of the lowest quality paper stock and consists of unsorted mixed papers obtained from office buildings, printing plants, and other commercial sources
2. High Grades	Papers which can substitute directly for wood pulp and are high quality fibers (2 classifications)
a. Pulp Substitutes	Clippings and shavings, such as envelopes and bleached board cuttings, and other quality fibers derived from paper converting plants and data processing centers (computer tab cards)
b. Deinking	Usually bleached papers that have gone through a printing operation and are collected from printing plants and other converters.

Miscellaneous Materials

CRANKCASE OIL is another name for drained motor oil. Impurities from the engine such as dirt, solvents, and various chemicals accumulate in the oil. Oil refineries can separate the impurities from the oil so that it can be reused. This prevents waste oils from being dumped into rivers and on land. It also helps conserve the oil supply.

Individuals and organizations wishing to recycle
used motor oil are encouraged to contact the manager of
the Used Oil Recovery Program, Emerging Technology Section
of the Illinois Department of Energy and Natural Resources
Room 300, 325 W. Adams St., Springfield IL 62706 for infor
mation on developing an oil recovery program and a listing
of used oil haulers, reprocessors, and rerefiners. Information can also be obtained from members of the Illinois
Association of Recycling Centers, P.O. Box 48761, Chicago
IL 60648.

PLASTICS are made from petroleum resources. They
are composed of complex molecular structures which makes
them essentially nonbiodegradable. This same structure
also makes recycling very difficult. Technology has not
yet been widely adapted that can upgrade waste plastics
into useful products. Scrap plastics have been recycled,
but mainly from inplant sources. The plastics industry
has been working to increase recycling, but progress has
been slow.

RUBBER TIRES - When considering tires, there should
first be a clear distinction between "used" tires and
"worn out" or "scrap" tires. "Used" tires are still
valuable for producing retreads. "Scrap" tires are too
worn to act as bases for retreads and, therefore, have
outlived their usefulness in the tire industry.

"Used" tires have been recycled for many years.
There are nearly 5000 recapping industries in the U.S.
Unfortunately, resources in Illinois are severely limited,
and the market for "scrap" tires is much bleaker.[9]

It's
Our
Choice
Preserve it
to deserve it !

Markets For The
Sale of Recyclables

> *"The entrepreneur finds those places that he can sneak into the marketplace that the large fellow doesn't want because it's too small, or he doesn't understand anyway. And so that's how the little guy gets big."*

The first step is to determine what materials will be recycled. Market conditions in the region will undoubtedly be the most influencing factor in this decision. One can recycle only that which can be sold or reused.

Recycling, first and foremost, is an economic activity The collection system which recovers materials must be supported by sale of the materials. Before you stimulate recycling efforts in your community, you must identify secure markets.

Recycled materials are sold both domestically and on international markets. The prices offered for recycled materials vary greatly; each commodity's price fluctuates differently. These fluctuations reflect the basic economic reality that supply is greater than market demand for recycled materials in this country.

Lack of markets for recycled materials can be devastating to a recycling program. Many recycling centers have been forced to close because they have not been able to sell, at an acceptable price, the materials they have recovered. As the long-used adage from the salvage industry indicates, *Scrap is not sold, it is bought*.

So, because of their dependence on the wider economy, waste materials markets are volatile; a gentle ripple in the national economy may generate severe waves through the recycling marketplace, forcing buyers to purchase only what they are confident they can sell.[10]

Recycling is impeded by a number of other factors. Organizations developing recycling programs and markets for recycled materials should be aware of the various federal, state, and local policies which have or may create barriers to recycling.

Recycled materials suffer from economic disadvantages due to depletion allowances and capital gains tax advantages given virgin materials. Industries such as paper manufacturing, which have companies producing both virgin paper and recycled paper, are subsidized by the federal government to invest in equipment that produces paper from virgin materials.

In the area of transportation, recycled materials have suffered for decades with freight rates established by the Interstate Commerce Commission. These rates favored the shipment of virgin materials. After almost a decade of fighting, the National Association of Recycling Industries scored their first major victories in 1980 on this issue. The U.S. Supreme Court upheld the Court of Appeals, which directed the Interstate Commerce Commission to revise their rates to a level of reasonableness. which is equivalent to rates of all other commodities that move by rail. This decision will enable recycled materials to compete more favorably with virgin materials by reducing their costs of shipment.

Zoning regulations have also thwarted the efforts of recycling operations to expand. Zoning restrictions, designed to limit the locations of scrap processors, have a negative impact on industrial recycling activities as well as on the community organization seeking to locate a site for convenient consumer recycling.

The key to finding markets for recycled materials will be public policies and other efforts which encourage expansion and development of industries using recycled materials in their manufacturing processes.

But what about the program you wish to begin? No matter how well developed a collection system may be, unless the recovered materials can be returned to productive use, recycling will fail. The key, then, to a successful recycling project is the identification of sufficient existing markets, or the development of new ones.[11]

Locating Markets

Before beginning, it is wise to conduct a market survey for your specific area. It is usually best to determine how the area rates in market potential for the most commonly recovered materials: glass, tin and bimetal cans, paper, and aluminum.

To aid in these efforts, obtain a copy of the *Illinois Directory of Environmental Information* from the Illinois Department of Energy and Natural Resources at 309 W. Washington, Chicago IL 60606. The directory contains a list of industries interested in purchasing recycled materials from community projects. Please note that as with any published list, there will be changes, additions and deletions. The industries listed in the directory have not committed themselves to buying scrap but have expressed interest. Limited though it may be, it is a good place to start.

Check the list for markets in cities near you. A general rule is to stay within a 100-mile radius of the community. The resale value of materials recovered from solid waste does not warrant shipping small volumes for distances greater than 100 miles.

By no means should the market survey be limited to the list in the directory. Check the yellow pages under "Junk Dealers," "Scrap Dealers," "Salvage Companies," "Paper Scrap," "Iron and Metals," "Glass Manufacturing," etc. for secondary dealers who may be a prime market.

Nearly every community has at least one scrap dealer who has the resources to economically store, compact, and transport large quantities of materials for distances greater than 100 miles. However, as a middleman, the secondary dealer must make a profit and usually the prices you will receive for your materials will be somewhat lower.[12]

It may not be possible to find an immediate buyer for the particular scrap in question, but persistence will usually "pay off." Markets may not be overwhelming in Illinois, but they are available, and a good market survey should bring them to light.

Additional resources which may be useful in locating markets for the sale of recyclable materials begin on the following page.

ADDITIONAL MARKET RESOURCES

ILLINOIS ASSOCIATION OF
 RECYCLING CENTERS
P.O. Box 48761
Chicago IL 60648

INDIANA STATE BOARD OF HEALTH
Solid Waste Management Section
Division of Sanitary Engineering
1330 W. Michigan Street
Indianapolis IN 46206

WISCONSIN STATE SOLID
 WASTE RECYCLING AUTHORITY
3321 W. Beltline Highway
Madison WI 53713

NATIONAL ASSOCIATION OF
 RECYCLING INDUSTRIES
330 Madison Avenue
New York, N.Y. 10017

PAPER STOCK CONSERVATION
 COMMITTEE
American Paper Institute
260 Madison Avenue
New York, N.Y. 10016

PAPER STOCK INSTITUTE OF
 AMERICA
330 Madison Avenue
New York, N.Y. 10017

GLASS PACKAGING INSTITUTE
2000 L. Street, N.W.
Washington D.C. 20006

THE ALUMINUM ASSOCIATION
818 Connecticut Ave., N.W.
Washington D.C. 20006

Contacting The Buyer

Contact possible markets and explain the project.
Many industries have become ecology minded in the past
few years and often are willing to support civic groups.
Learn of their individual specifications for the scrap;
in other words: how must the materials be prepared for
delivery to them? Remember, one cannot sell garbage!
Unless the materials meet specifications, it is considered to be "garbage."

Next, arrange for special meetings with company representatives to open communications. It is much easier
to turn a person down by phone than in person. In dealing with buyers, learn marketing terms, price structures,
and industry processes so that there will be no confusion.
Many industries can accept greater levels of scrap input
than they do now. Many industries also tolerate larger
percentages of contaminants than they will readily admit.

The marketing goal, at this point, will be to secure
a firm commitment of "intent to buy" from a buyer prior
to inception of your project. Large mechanical resource
recovery facilities are securing formal "letters of intent
to purchase from potential markets. These are legal
documents citing a buyer's intention to buy the recovered
materials after the facility is constructed.

You may be able to secure this type of document, or
a least a formal letter, from the company explaining its
intent to buy. Don't be discouraged though if you are
not able to secure this. Many recycling projects have
relied on informal agreements and been successful. Don't
be overly optimistic about what prices or quantities the
buyer will accept at first. Remember, you may be pen-
etrating a market for the first time.

Once you have made arrangements for the purchase of
your materials, don't forget to learn details such as
what hours the purchaser can receive the materials, how
they should be delivered, and terms of payment.[13]

Marketing Strategies

As a general rule, open market and contractual sales
agreements are the two major marketing arrangements implemented.

Where more than one independent buyer exists, open
market arrangements have both advantages and limitations.
Reliance on the open market requires a stable condition.
You will need to carefully gauge the depth and reliability
of a particular market situation. What has the range of
prices been in the recent past? How many potential buyers
are available? How long have they been in continuous
business?

Given market stability, an open sales strategy can allow a group to achieve higher prices due to the flexibility of the marketplace. In addition, it allows for the switch of buyers in the case of deteriorating relationships or inadequate service. But open market trading does require managerial control, and lack of stability must be accepted. Realization of top prices during the best of times must be balanced against recognition of potential high losses during market weakness.

The issue is basic: should you trade off the possible high profits of the open market against the possible catastrophe of declining demand by marketing under a contract? Contract sales will likely mean lower prices during a strong market.

Typical contracts include minimum tonnage requirements with a penalty clause for lack of specific volume, the period of the agreement, purchase specifications, and the pricing structure. Advantages of the contract market structure include the guaranteed pricing system plus the likelihood of higher quality service from the buyer in the forms of technical advice, handling equipment, and storage containers. On the otherhand, the inflexible nature of the agreement may create severe pressures during high market conditions.[14]

Which ever strategy you choose, a note of caution is needed here. Many recycling projects have failed because their operators did not institute marketing, sales, and income controls. While negotiating and trading with secondary materials buyers, be sure to keep clear written records. You should not jeopardize your project's success with lazy business practices. Be sure to study this guide's chapter on BUSINESS MANAGEMENT carefully.

How to Organize
Your Recycling Program

One person can spark a recycling project, but no one can do the job alone. You'll need help and lots of it. If you are already part of an organization or group, you have a starting nucleus for your program. Build around it. Working together in coalition means stronger leadership and less duplication of effort.

Get in touch with all organizations in your town -- civic, youth, business, service, area, etc. Your Chamber of Commerce should have listings of these. Some organizations to contact:

Church Groups
Service Clubs
League of Women Voters
Board of Education and
  other educational groups
Conservation People
Labor Unions
Professional Organizations
Merchants Organizations
Volunteer Bureaus
Mayor's Office
PTA's
United Fund/ Community
  Chest
All Communications Media

Jaycees
Boy and Girl Scouts
Boys' and Girls' Clubs
Campfire Girls
Key Clubs
YMCA, YWCA Youth Groups
School Service & Science Clubs
City Youth Board
City Environmental/Beautification/
  or Improvement Commissions
4-H Clubs
Future Farmers of America
Other "Futures" Groups
Community Action Groups
Civil Right Organizations[15]

It should be added that inner-city minorities or the poor are seldom involved with community recycling ventures In trying to analyze why inner-city groups are often not part of organizations working on solid waste management issues, speculation has to substitute for fact.

It may well be that organizations representing minorities and the city poor often feel they must concentrate their energies on the struggle for better housing, jobs, and education. Leaders may see the importance of staving off the decline of environmental quality, but most inner-city residents are likely to have more immediate concerns. Without a doubt, citizens groups need to concentrate more on reaching out to involve all community residents in efforts to improve solid waste management policies and practices.

The next step to organizing your recycling project will be to:

Organize A Committee

The committee should reflect the various segments of the community and be composed of dependable people. You will need perseverent individuals able and willing to fulfill the following roles:

COORDINATOR:
Management, including contact with scrap dealers; respond to inquiries; fundraising; leading the group

COMMUNITY RELATIONS:
Contacting community groups, local government agencies, local businesses for help; getting donations; public appearances; publicity; promotion; advertising, etc.

PHYSICAL ARRANGEMENTS:
Securing collection site(s); obtaining storage containers for scrap, safety glasses, gloves, other equipment

PROCESSING:
Day-to-day handling of materials; sorting, preparing, stacking

TRANSPORTATION:
Making arrangements to haul used materials to scrap dealers; pick-ups for elderly or other special requests; securing special transportation vehicles and equipment

<u>RECRUITING</u>:
Finding and training help needed to operate the site

<u>BUSINESS MANAGEMENT</u>:
Keeping records of costs, issue of disbursements and
receipts, shipment records; maintaining legal status;
coordinate compliance with ordinances

Site Selection

You have researched the scrap markets and formed
your committee. All is moving along smoothly. Now you
are prepared to seek out a site for locating your recycling
project. The site must be located in your community or
close to it. It must be large enough to store the materials you will be collecting. It must be easily accessible
from the street.

If the site is outdoors, it should be fenced or
otherwise protected to keep children from playing with
the materials, and you will need some form of cover to
protect your recyclables from the rain and snow.

Situating your collection point in an area where
people do not have to make a special trip and can
accomplish several necessary activities at once is
highly desireable. A good rule of thumb is to locate
your project at a distance of no more than three miles
from the people you hope will participate.

Use your local "people" resources for assistance in
locating a site. Don't forget about public works or
planning department personnel, commercial realtors, the
Chamber of Commerce, and other local citizens groups.

Think about the following as possible locations when
considering a <u>permanent</u> recycling depot.

Landfill Site	Old Military Installation
Empty Storefront	Small Industrial Park
Church Parish House	Warehouse Loading Dock
Fire Stations	City Hall
Large Service Station	Municipal Parking Lot

Be creative! Locating a site is sometimes difficult -- especially in a city where land costs are at a premium. But if you look carefully and with perseverence, it should be possible to locate land on a rent-free or low-cost basis

For a _temporary_ site, locate your depot in or at a:

Home Garage*   School Parking Lot
Shopping Center   Fairgrounds
Vacant Lot

* Check to make certain this would not be a violation of
  a city zoning ordinance.

Physical Set-Up

The physical set-up of your site will be determined by the type(s) of material you collect, the nature of your project (supervised/unsupervised, open daily/once a month), size and nature of the equipment you will need, and your workforce.

The drawings which follow on the next three pages will offer ideas for site set-up. Each is scaled to give you a perspective on how much space is commonly used for various functions.

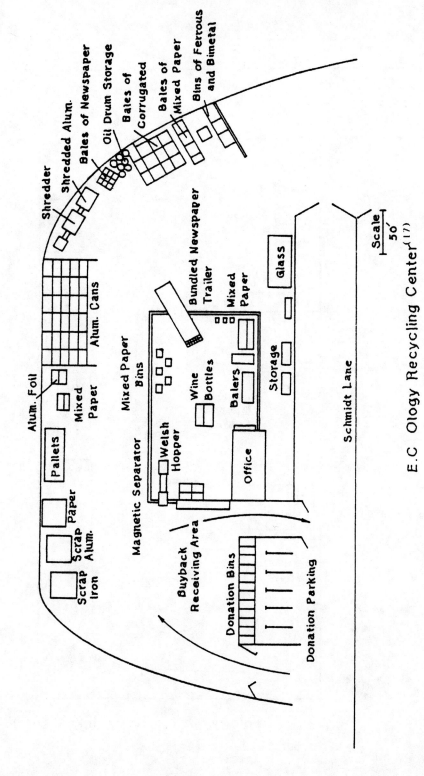

E.C Ology Recycling Center[(17)]

33

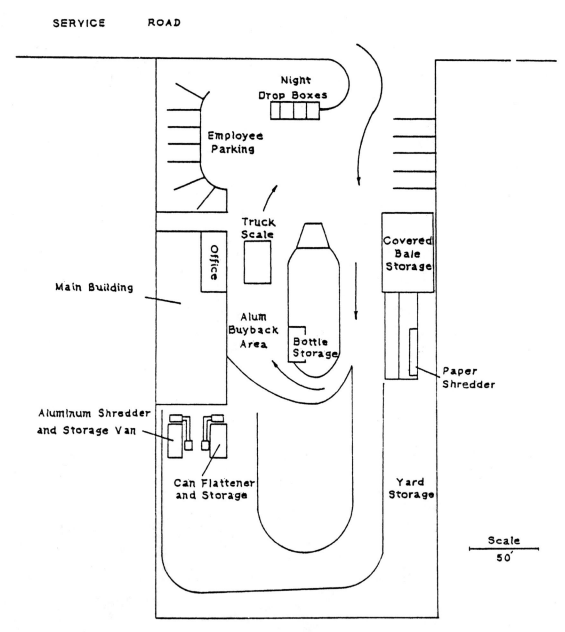

SERVICE ROAD

Night Drop Boxes

Employee Parking

Truck Scale

Office

Main Building

Alum Buyback Area

Bottle Storage

Covered Bale Storage

Paper Shredder

Aluminum Shredder and Storage Van

Can Flattener and Storage

Yard Storage

Scale 50'

Ecology Action Recycling Center

34

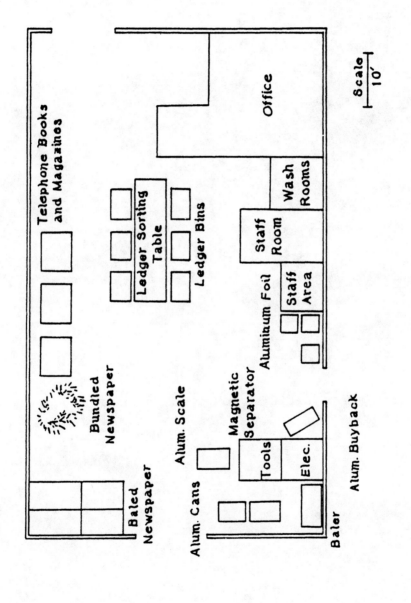

Ecology Action's Main Building [19]

Scale
10'

35

Models of Operation

There is no one model way of operating a recycling center. Many successful recycling projects in Illinois have changed their operations as other factors influencing their programs have altered. If your mind is not open to such change, your project will become as extinct as the dinosaur. Successful recycling is usually an evolutionary process. Rarely does a project begin with all its operational needs fulfilled.

Most groups start out small, collecting one or two types of materials in barrels or boxes, accomplishing the hauling task through the efforts of a well-wishing neighbor with a pick-up truck. As an example of the level of simplicity which is possible, one Illinois couple collects and stores recyclables collected from the community on their farm. They sell to a variety of nearby markets when quantities warrent the trip in their pick-up truck, and because theirs is not a commercial enterprise, proceeds from material sales are donated to local charities. You can do it too, or you can develop your project around a variety of operational alternatives.

Drop-Off Centers

Drop-off centers are stationary collection points or depots set up to receive materials from the public for recycling. Few centers are alike since most are set up to make the most efficient use of local resources. A drop-off center is very flexible in the types of materials it can handle. You will need considerable space for collection and storage if you plan the project to be a full-service (collecting glass, metals, paper products, oil, etc.) project, and much less space will be needed for the collection of fewer materials.

The major advantage to operating a drop-off center is the possibility for 24-hour access. Donors will be able to bring their recyclables to the site at hours most convenient to them. However, it should be noted that if you allow 24-hour access to the site, you will have to take steps to prevent crime. Vandalism may occur after dark, and as the value of recyclables materials increases, so does the rate of theft.

Drop-off centers can be classified into two major types: unmanned and manned.

The unmanned drop-off center is likely to be located at schools, churches, apartment complexes, shopping centers, or vacant lots. This method is most commonly used by community organizations for their fundraising projects. Donors deliver their recyclables and separate them into appropriate bins -- hopefully. Because an attendent is not available, collection containers must be especially sturdy, safely constructed, and well marked with instructions for the public.

Running an unmanned drop-off center has the advantage of low or no labor cost or volunteer management problems. On the other hand, your chances of receiving trash and other unwanted materials is increased because no attendent is available to assist and educate the public If your unattended project is not well protected, you may run into problems to those similar with the 24-hour projects. And if it is located near a school or other location where its access is open to youngsters, local police may dub your program an "attractive nuisance."

The manned or attended drop-off center has definite advantages. The center is staffed and emphasis is often given to the educational aspects of recycling. Having staff, whether paid or voluntary, presents the opportunity to assist, instruct, and answer donors' questions. During the time an attendent is available, theft and vandalism will not be a problem, but don't forget about the off hours.

Contact your local police chief and request that patrols in your area keep an eye open for problems. Be sure to give them the name and phone number of someone to contact in case of an emergency. Of course, this is good advice no matter what type of recycling project you conduct.

The manned drop-off center may have higher operating costs than the unmanned depot. If your staff is paid, you will have the added expense of not only salaries, but payroll taxes and insurance as well. If your staff is voluntary, you will have the expense of volunteer recruitment and training.

Remember, factors between projects can vary dramatically. Only you and your committee can weigh the pros and cons and choose which aspects will play a more important role in your particular situation.

Periodic Or Permanent Collections

The manned and unmanned collection methods described above can be implemented on either a periodic or permanent basis.

Periodic projects are operated on a "once-in-a while" basis or on a regular schedule, e.g., the second Saturday of each month from 10 a.m. to 2 p.m. With a periodic set-up, a large truck often serves as a mobile "depot" hauling all the recyclables away at closing time. The periodic collection project makes scheduling of staff or volunteers quite simple and has the added advantage of offering little opportunity for a mess to develop. One drawback is that the public must stick to your schedule, and they may not be available when you are. Another is that you must make arrangements for material storage or haul recyclables directly to market.

A permanent recycling project can operate on either a 24-hour or controlled access basis, but it is available to the public more frequently than the periodic project. This mode of operations necessitates that a permanent site be available, sometimes a difficulty in congested urban areas. Maintenance of the collection site is an ever-important issue when operating a permanent recycling program because the ongoing recycling center is constantly in the public eye. Do yourself, your neighbors, and re-cycling a favor by keeping your site neat, clean, and safe.

Single and Multi-Item Depots

Recycling collection centers or depots take several forms, ranging in size and complexity from small newspaper collection bins in the corners of parking lots to huge ongoing projects collecting many tons of waste per week.

Depots accepting only one item usually show a profit. These kinds of projects include the newspaper or glass drop-offs run by various civic groups -- Lions, Kiwanis, Scouts, and the like. Costs are minimal in such projects because land and storage bins are usually donated and volunteers normally operate the program. Transportation to market is the only major expense, and the revenues go to the worthy causes of the sponsoring organizations.

Other kinds of depots take as many varieties as they feel they can market. The groups operating these recycling projects are usually nonprofit corporations engaging in recycling because of concern with general environmental issues and in particular with the solid waste problem.

In terms of economy, multi-item depots require a larger work-force than single item depots. Each item accepted requires a different form of processing and entails a separate kind of handling.

The Pick-Up Service

Many organizations that have mastered the techniques of operating a collection depot will expand their programs to include a pick-up service. Pick-ups can be made on an on-call basis, a regular residential route can be estab-lished, and commercial businesses can be served. Pick-ups can be made using a private auto or a large truck -- that, of course, depends on what materials and what quantity you expect to pick-up.

ON-CALL PICK-UPS are often made on special occasions for people who don't have enough materials to pick-up on a regular basis. However, you will not want to invest your time and gasoline to pick up a dozen bottles or one stack of newspapers. Set standards and enforce them. Make certain your requirements for amount and preparation of materials are clearly understood. Do not hesitate to refuse a caller if the distance is too great or the amount too small to cover your costs.

REGULAR RESIDENTIAL ROUTES can be very productive for collecting large amounts of materials on a regular basis. You will want to do extensive publicity before you begin a program of this type. Let your donors know what materials are acceptable, how they need to be prepared, where to leave them (curbside, doorstep, alley, etc.), and when your collection is scheduled. Distributing a calendar schedule is a helpful and inexpensive reminder to the households on your route.

Do remember that it can be disasterous for developing an ongoing residential route if you don't pick-up materials when promised. If, on occasion, delays or changes in your schedule occur, inform your donors immediately. One additional piece of advice -- begin with small routes expanding only as your resources allow. And be considerate of your staff or volunteers; picking up bundles of recyclables and loading them into a truck is strenuous work. Would you be able to do it for more than a couple of hours at a time? If not, don't expect that your workers will be able to do so either.

A COMMERCIAL PICK-UP PROGRAM can be a big plus to your project because large volumes of recyclables can be picked up on only one trip. Office waste paper, glass, and corrugated cardboard are common business recyclables.

Waste disposal costs for businesses are high and herein lies the greatest motivation for commercial establishments to participate in your program. Volume requirements are usually easy for businesses to meet, but here you also need to be specific about your preparation requirements. You will want the materials to be as "clean" as possible, but try to be flexible because to business people time is money. If you pick up glass from a tavern, for example, you may receive many liquor bottles with metal rings attached. If your donor feels it takes too much time for removal of the rings, you may be able to do so once you bring the materials to your storage site. However, in this case, you will have to insist that the bottles are unbroken for safety in handling.

In the case of corrugated cardboard, another high volume waste item for businesses, you will want the boxes broken down and bundled in some way. One Chicago-land recycling project refurbishes old, used balers and rents them out to businesses at very low rates. The organization, in turn, pays the business a small amount for their baled cardboard. They are able to do so, and thereby encourage the participation of more businesses, because the organization's handling costs are lowered and greater volume can be collected on one trip when the cardboard is baled.

The Buy-Back Program

Many recycling program operators nationwide have found that they can greatly increase the volumes of materials they receive by paying the public small amounts for their goods. Operating a buy-back program is only recommended if your project is well established in all respects. More equipment is needed for storage; a scale becomes an absolute necessity. Your staff must be well trained and able to handle cash, and your bookkeeping system must be on a highly professional level.

Before you consider implementing a buy-back program, consult a lawyer about the possible effect of this action on your organization's tax-exempt status. IRS law states that your group's income is only tax free if it is obtained through activities in agreement with your organization's legal tax-exempt purpose. The opinion of a legal expert is very important here because there is no definitive IRS ruling regarding the acceptability of nonprofit-operated buy-back programs.

Remember also, once you have established a buy-back program, you may be in direct competition with local scrap dealers. The prices you pay the public must be competitive you must cover your operating costs. And yet, you do not want to alienate possible market sources for your group. You can read more about buy-back programs in our section on RECYCLING AND ECONOMIC DEVELOPMENT which begins in this guide on page 119.

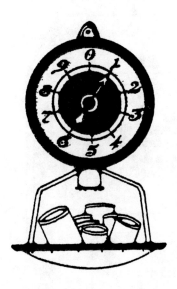

Processing,
Equipment,
and Transportation

Preparing the recyclable materials you collect to the specifications of the market to which you will sell is essential. If the load of materials you ship to market is rejected, you will most likely have to dump it at the landfill. Not only will such a rejection be a setback to your organization's morale, your group's pocketbook will be negatively impacted as well. You will lose the value of the scrap, experience increased transportation costs in hauling to the dump, and in many cases, you will pay a dumping fee as well. You will need to plan and prepare carefully to avoid these setbacks.

Earlier in this guide (pages 15-21), we discussed the recyclable materials most often collected by community recycling centers. Note the common specifications described in this section and plan your project accordingly

You will want to educate your patrons to the extent that most of the materials are processed by them, at home, before the items are brought to your collection area. But even under the best of circumstances, some processing must be done at the depot.

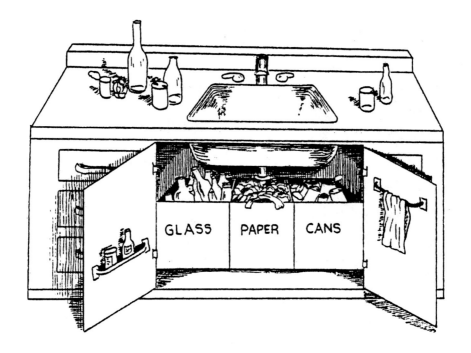

Teach your donors to prepare their materials at home
before bringing them to the recycling center.

The following discussion of equipment, tools, and
transportation will offer you suggestions on ways of
making the task of handling your recyclables more man-
ageable. Also remember that experience is the best
teacher, so find out from other local projects which
equipment and systems have worked for them and put
their experience to work for you.

Equipment and Handling

Whatever type of recycling project you choose to
operate, you will need equipment to handle the materials
and containers in which to store and transport them.
Try to get as many donations as possible. Depending on
the type of project, you will need some or all of the
following: recycling information handouts, signs; first
aid kit; brooms, dustpan, scoop shovel and trash can for
non-recyclables; and heavy protective gloves. Other
equipment needs depend on what materials you collect.

GLASS: Wooden drum covers with holes to accomodate long-handled sledges if you plan to break glass manually; safety glasses or goggles; church key, pliers, or a similar tool to remove metal rings from bottle necks.

CANS: Sledges or road tamper to crush cans; can opener to remove ends of cans; magnet to test metal types. Remember, aluminum is not magnetic.

NEWSPAPER: Twine and scissors to tie bundles.

Once your newspaper volume has built up, a banding tool and bundler for handling cardboard and bundling loose paper become invaluable additions to your operation. Recyclers tell us that the banding tool can be put to a variety of repair and miscellaneous uses. Both machines can often be rented at low rates from a paper broker who might even provide them free of charge for your use.

Moving heavy containers in and out of a truck presents special difficulties and requires the use of rollers, lift trucks, chain blocks, hand trucks, lift gates, and/or winch booms. If you are going to transport your own materials, you will need a pick-up or larger truck. If your volume is very low, you might get away with cardboard boxes in a station wagon.

Containers

Recyclers utilize a wide variety of containers for collecting, storing and shipping their materials. These include metal and fiber drums, wood pallet boxes and crates, cardboard boxes, 5-gallon paint cans for crushed glass, plastic bags and burlap sacks for tin cans, steel bins, drop boxes, dump trucks, and truck trailers.

Factors to consider in your choice of containers include:

1) Availability;

2) Buyer's requirements and compatability with unloading system at markets;

3) Whether storage is indoors or out;

4) Availability of handling equipment;

5) Whether ground surface is soft or hard, even or bumpy; and

6) Type of transportation vehicle.

An empty 55-gallon metal drum weighs anywhere from 15 to 90 pounds, averaging about 50 pounds. Fiber barrels offer an obvious advantage when the empty barrels must be moved often. Fiber barrels weigh from 5 to 20 pounds, usually about 15 pounds for the 40-gallon size. 55-gallon steel drums or fiber barrels can be obtained free or for a small charge from many companies that discard them. Try fuel oil companies, construction firms, paint companies, bakeries, and chemical companies.

Leave your supply of empty barrels upside down until you want to use them so that people won't put things in every barrel. Fiber barrels and boxes should be kept out of the rain. It is also handy to have holes in your steel barrels so that rainwater can run out and you may want to paint the insides of metal barrels with a rust preventative paint to keep metallic rust particles from contaminating any glass you may store in them.

Sometimes handling of materials is simplified by using the trailer from a semi-truck as the container at the collection site. Dump trucks and drop boxes are also used. This works well for newspaper drives and could also be used for collection of a high volume of glass or cans. A waste paper company may loan one of these for collecting paper, leaving it in a parking lot until full, then hauling it away. Often such projects are unattended and signs should be erected which instruct the public on how to load the materials for proper weight distribution.

The following chart will give you an idea of the capacities and site requirements of such containers.

	Maximum Capacity	Location Requirements
SEMI-TRAILER	20 Tons	2 x 6 planks must be placed under front dolly wheels to prevent damage to pavement
DROP-BOX (Large)	8-12 Tons	Hard surface lot with 40-50 feet of straight running space for positioning
DROP-BOX (Small)	8-10 Tons	Hard surface lot with 40-50 feet of straight running space for positioning.

A note of caution about using semi-trailers or drop-boxes -- you will certainly want to load as much paper into these containers as possible to maximize your profit, but overloading can cause a safety hazard and damage the surface on which the container stands.

To prevent trailer overload, papers should be stacked to a maximum height of seven feet. To prevent front end overload, begin by stacking one row of papers to within one foot of the top and along each side of the trailer. You can then go back and fill in from the sides.

Additional Equipment

In 1980, the U. S. Environmental Protection Agency published a guide entitled, *Source Separation Collection and Processing Equipment* (Pub. No. SW-842, Office of Solid Waste). This guide will be invaluable for organizations ready to develop more sophisticated systems. The publication summarizes advantages and disadvantages of various pieces of equipment, lists manufacturers' specifications, and suppliers of equipment useful to the recycling center operator.

We recommend this publication highly to those interested in exploring the possible use of the following types of equipment.

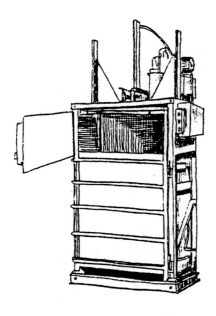

BALERS for use in compacting paper products or metals for easier handling and volume reduction

GLASS CRUSHERS -
Over-the-barrel and hammermill crushers offer advantages to groups that ship glass in low volume containers or trucks

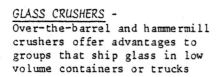

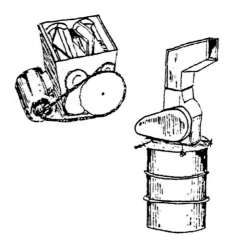

CAN FLATTENERS AND MAGNETIC
SEPARATORS are invaluable if
you handle large volumes of
metals

FORK LIFT TRUCKS are needed
if heavy bins or barrels
must be picked up for
loading or unloading

SELF-DUMPING HOPPERS are used
by many recyclers for collection and storage of materials

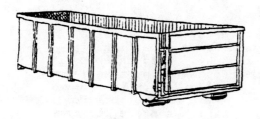

REFUSE CONTAINERS OR DROP-BOXES
are convenient for collecting
large volume materials such
as glass and newspaper.

About Trucking and Transportation

* Try to balance trucking costs and estimated income from recyclables.

* If it is determined that recycling will save the city collection and disposal costs, the city maintenance department may be willing to transport materials and conduct special pick-ups.

* Write or call markets in nearby major cities to see if they have trucks passing through the area regularly which might pick-up the materials.

* Check out insurance coverage on offers of privately-owned vehicles.

* A trucking firm may donate space on a "dead run" (when the truck carries no cargo) and charge for mileage or the trucker's salary only.

* Businesses that use carting trucks or rental companies might lend the recycling center a truck.

* Contact Army Reserve units, the National Guard, private individuals to locate a donated truck or station wagon.

* Some companies might supply a truck and driver to haul materials during the weekend when they will not be using the trucks.

NOTE: Dump trucks are ideal, but pick-up trucks will suffice. The type of truck you will need will depend on the volume collected, the condition of the material collected, and the distance materials must be transported. If there is no loading dock at the collection site, a truck with a hydraulic lift on the tailgate is helpful, especially if drums or crushed glass must be moved. Make certain that trucks are well covered to prevent waste spillage and that they are not loaded beyond roadway weight limits.[21]

Before taking materials to a buyer, it is always a good idea to check to be certain he is accepting what you have to sell on a particular day. Also check by telephone on the buyer's current open-hours; these sometimes change without notice. Finally, check your buyer's current price before you deliver; you may be able to store some items until you can obtain a higher price for them. At least one worker should go along with the truck driver to assist with unloading.

The procedure at most scrap brokers' establishments is to drive onto a scale and tell the scale operator what type of material you have. He will then tell you where to unload; then return to the scale for reweighing. Some brokers will pay you in cash and others will forward a check to your organization at a future date. Be sure to get a copy of the weight tickets -- both full and empty -- so that no confusion will develop over the amount of payment due and to facilitate your financial and volume recordkeeping.

Legal Requirements to be Considered

Check with local officials to see:

* if a license and/or zoning variance is needed to run the depot.

* if the center is in compliance with fire, safety, health, sign, and nuisance abatement ordinances.

* if the center picks up materials, is it infringing on a garbage collection franchise? If so, try to reach an agreement with the local collector.

* if trucking permits to haul recyclables are needed.

* if the center is a home operation, what special requirments are made of it be city or county?

* if the center is municipally-sponsored, can it get state tax credits or float a bond issue when acquiring equipment and facilities?

General Legal Information

Some local governments have restrictions on home storage of paper, the parking of trucks, the outside storage of barrels (if the depot is set up in a private home).

If the center is storing newspaper inside a city's limits, it may be required to have a metal rather than a wooden building (or at least metal containers for paper).

All regulations should be checked to determine whether or not the operation is a legal one. If the regulations appear to be unfair, discuss the problem with officials. Chances are the laws were not designed to cover recycling operations and they may be able to be interpreted differently for such programs.

A major legal problem encountered by many recyclers stems from the practice of classifying a recycling project as a junk or salvage yard. This often prevents recycling centers from being set up in a residential or commercial neighborhood. The following argument may be helpful to get out of this.

A recycling center is unlike a junk yard in many ways. It is a public service and not a retail or wholesale business. The processing is minimal compared to what is done by a junk yard due to the limited type of materials taken in. Materials move through much faster than in most junk yards. It is a community service and must be convenient to the public in order to exist.[22]

Managing Your Human Resources

Throughout pages 29-31 of this manual, we discussed how to organize a committee to take charge of operating your recycling project. This committee is the nucleus of your program, and the functions performed by these people are crucial to the success of an ongoing project.

Once again, you will need people -- paid or voluntary -- to fulfill the following roles: coordinator, community relations, physical arrangements, processing, transportation recruiting, and business management. You will need to plan your project around the labor resources available in your community.

In some small scale projects such as unstaffed depots, the functions listed above may be managed by one or two people. Full-line recycling centers and repeating projects require more help and usually become the projects of groups. Very few recycling projects begin with sufficient financial resources to pay workers from the outset. Most begin with volunteers help, and as the projects expand, some keep their volunteer labor or initiate a payroll.

In either case, the goal becomes clear. You must manage your human resources wisely by striving to get the right person into the right job at the right time. To achieve this goal, attaining broad community support should be the aim of all projects that want a long life.

One excellent local example of an organization utilizing broad community support is the McHenry County Defenders of Crystal Lake, Illinois.

Because of the amount of labor needed to implement the project effectively, the Defenders enlist the aid of a large variety of community groups. In Crystal Lake, Boy Scout Troop 127 regularly handles glass collections. For their efforts, the Scouts receive all revenues from the sale of this material. Tin and aluminum cans and used motor oil are handled by members of the Defenders, and proceeds from the sale of these materials supports their ongoing projects. Proceeds for paper collections are shared by the Defenders and other community groups which provide labor. In the City of McHenry, also served by the Defenders project, all materials are processed by Defender members with the help of local organizations. The groups then split revenues.

The McHenry County Defenders believe that community involvement is the key to their program's success. Each group that participates encourages new people to recycle their bottles, cans, newspapers, and used oil. You can read more about the McHenry County Defenders in this guides section called, "RECYCLING FOCUS."

Another northern Illinois program has found an alternative solution to its labor needs. The North Shore Ecology Center (NSEC), based in Highland Park, Illinois, operates ten recycling locations in nine communties and the program still continues to grow. NSEC has opted for using paid staff because of the size and diversity of their project. In an NSEC-owned truck, a crew of one to three paid employees make daily rounds of each of the ten recycling depots to take care of any needed materials processing and site maintenance.

More information about the North Shore Ecology Center can also be found in the "RECYCLING FOCUS" section. Here you will also find profiles of other Illinois recycling groups with information on who is doing what.

Who Volunteers and Why?

The spirit of volunteering -- of one person helping another -- goes back to the beginning of human history. Perhaps it has been *the* humanizing element, parent helping child, child assisting parent, neighbor aiding neighbor. Whether it has meant taking turns guarding the entrance to the cave, throwing down your cloak for the queen to pass, joining with friends to raise a barn roof, or coming together to run a community recycling center -- volunteers speak loud and clear on their own behalf.

This age-old willingness to help others has matured. The spirit of wanting to take an active part in building a stronger, saner society, of wishing to restore, rehabilitate, improve, create, and re-create has come of age. At the same time, as more and more individuals have the time and concern to volunteer their abilities in a meaningful way, the more impact the new volunteerism has upon the nation.

Between 1965 and 1974, the number of volunteers in this country almost doubled. The ACTION/Census Bureau study *Americans Volunteer 1974* provides a profile of who volunteers and why. Although the largest group of volunteers falls into the 25 to 54 age bracket, teenagers and retired people also volunteer in significant numbers. According to statistics, one out of every five American men volunteer, and increasing numbers of nonwhites are volunteering. The ACTION survey revealed that more employed people are active volunteers than unemployed people. There is also a positive correlation between volunteering and income level and length of formal education. This ever greater diversity of people willing and able to work without pay represents a rich staffing resource for all types of communtiy projects.

Volunteering can serve to enhance the self-image of the one who volunteers. Social scientists have found that low self-esteem is at the root of many social and educational problems as well as individual antisocial and self-destructive behavior at all socio-economic levels Thus, volunteering can be an essential human developmental experience when it meets this universal need for self-esteem.

Volunteering offers diverse opportunities for self-discovery and learning. For students, volunteering provides the field experience necessary to apply and test classroom theories. For women whose careers have been interupted, volunteering provides an opportunity for re-evaluation. For workers in dull, routine jobs, volunteering can provide some of the intangible rewards they are missing in their paid work. For retired people looking for new ways to use accumulated wisdom, volunteering may offer the richest reward of all -- a new role.

As might be expected, the diversity of expectation and experience which characterizes volunteers is reflected in their approach to service. Some volunteers prefer to work independently in self-help or issue-oriented ad hoc groups. Often they work intensely on specific problems for a short period of time. Other volunteers, particularly those with solid professional role models, rely on strong staff support, expecting appropriate learning opportunities in established organizations.

General Tools for Recruiting

The common denominator in all aspects of a successful volunteer program is the successful recruitment of volunteers. Prospective volunteers come knocking at organization doors only occasionally. More commonly, the recruiter, you, must go out into the community to find the volunteer.

There are two basic things a recruiter must know: what the project's needs are and what the community has to offer in human resources. Then the recruiter can begin to plan the methods to be used to reach the potential volunteer and match the volunteer to the job.

Knowing Your Community
And Its Human Resources

The community surrounding your organization offers many types of resources, and it is a good idea to take inventory periodically. Here are a few basic questions to help you assess your resources. Add to this list those resources that may be unique to your situation.

* What kind of corporate community is available
  to you? Are business and industry seeking ways
  to meet pressures of social responsibility?
  Do you have volunteer opportunities to interest
  individual employees after work or on weekends?
  Are there other ways -- like artwork, printing,
  leftover or overstocked supplies, sponsorship
  of a particular project or event?

* Are many local community residents blue collar
  workers who may work on shifts and have time
  available when you badly need help?

* Is there a Chamber of Commerce or other similar
  council of local merchants where you can get
  helpful information about the business, industry,
  and civic side of your community?

* Is there a community college or other higher
  educational facility nearby? What about the
  local high school? Don't overlook these resources
  for finding leaders for training volunteers or
  staff, for available meeting rooms, as well as
  students as potential volunteers.

* Look for people where you are most apt to find
  them -- in laundromats, bowling alleys, super-
  markets, and pool rooms. They may let you use
  a corner of the bulletin board for a spot
  announcement.

* High rise apartments are also likely places to
  find people who are potential volunteers. Laundry
  rooms or lobby areas may yield bulletin board
  space also.

* Are there other organizations in your community
  that also recruit for volunteers? Could you
  combine efforts?

* Your community includes your recycling center
  donor. Many become great volunteers because
  who better knows the benefit of your service?

* Don't be shy about asking people to give their
  time and talents to your organization. It's a
  compliment to them, and don't prejudge their
  answer. Too many times we say "he won't do it,
  she's too busy" and then find they certainly
  would have if they had just been asked.[23]

Involving the Uninvolved in Volunteering

There are ways you can get the uninvolved person to become or continue to be a volunteer in your organization.

* Show the real need you have for his or her services. Be honest. Do not glamorize or minimize the assignment.

* Create an atmosphere of acceptance. Let the person know you are happy to have them as part of your team.

* Even the best volunteer may miss a day or two. Accept this as part of the scheme of things, but make it clear that you missed them.

* Differentiate between work and social time, but remember that socializing is very important. Volunteering should be fun.

* Involve the volunteer in planning for the work to be done. The person who shuns clubs and community groups may welcome the opportunity to be the one in charge of a special part of the project.

* Don't try to push a group or individual into accepting as assignment. They might say yes out of desperation and then leave the scene as soon as possible.

* Broaden the knowledge of local people about your project. Let people know that your organization is working to solve problems affecting them.

* Create a consciousness of need for help. Convince local residents in your community of the reality of the need for help.

* Show benefits that can be derived from the effort of those helping. What does a volunteer gain as a result of volunteering for your project?

* Promise a good character and business reference when a volunteer does a good job for you. And advertise the fact that this reference has value to a future employee.

* Don't take volunteers for granted. Express your appreciation frequently. An occasional party, picnics, free food and drink, recycling T-shirts, ecology patches, token gifts, or similar gestures will help keep up the esprit des corps.

A Word of Caution

You should not take the dependability of volunteers for granted. The best of intentions have been known to yield to the temptation of a sunny day. Some experienced recyclers recommend using volunteers only for well-defined tasks of short duration. As you get to know your volunteers, you will learn which ones can be counted on.

Tax Benefits for Volunteers

Because your volunteers give a great deal of time, talent, and energy to your project, be sure they are aware of the number of tax benefits available to them under the general charitable contribution deduction of the Internal Revenue Code. Volunteers may deduct unreimbursed expenditures made incident to giving services to a qualifying nonprofit 501(c)(3) organization.

The following are representative types of expenditures that may be deducted:

* Automobile mileage (at actual expense or 7¢ per mile standard rate)

* Bus and cab transportation expense

* Parking and tolls

* Special uniforms

* Telephone bills

* Entertainment and meals for others

* Costs of meals and lodging if away overnight

* Travel expenses above per dien allowance

* Tickets for charity benefits (above actual value)

The following may not be deducted:

* Value of volunteer time

* Dependent care expenses

* Your own meals and entertainment (unless away overnight)

A complete description of federal tax deductions for volunteers can be obtained from the local IRS Taxpayer Assistance Service. Ask for Publication #526, "Income Tax Deduction for Contributions."

Paid Workers

Recycling programs often require a whole spectrum of business duties that may demand more time and effort, possibly more skill than a volunteer can contribute.

If you plan to use paid staff, an attractive, competitive wage is necessary to retain interested and qualified personnel. While many recycling programs started with people who were willing to work for subsistence wages, this is becoming less and less common as recycling operations become more advanced and develop into an industry in its own right. If you are hiring people to operate glass crushers, balers or other potentially dangerous machinery, you will find the need to pay appealing wages especially true.[25]

In addition to recruiting and hiring, some of the following personnel-related responsibilities will be of concern to your organization as well.

1. To classify jobs and prepare wage and salary scales

2. To counsel employees

3. To deal with disciplinary problems

4. To develop safety standards and practices

5. To manage benefit programs, such as group insurance, health, and retirement plans

6. To provide for periodic reviews of the performance of each individual employee, and for recognition of his or her strengths and needs for further development

7. To assist individuals in their efforts to develop and qualify for more advanced work

8. To plan and supervise training programs [26]

Some Final Words on Staffing

The size and nature of your program will help
determine your labor needs. But remember that qualified
and valuable help, volunteer or hired, does not come
automatically. You must be willing and prepared to
train and instruct your labor force in materials handling
public assistance, education, and safety procedures.

Remember also that human resource management is
concerned with the effective use of the skills of people.
The all-important word here is *PEOPLE*. Whether your
people are volunteers or paid workers, most psychologists
agree that there are certain desires (and needs) for
every person at every age and station of life. Remember
these desires and needs to build a foundation of mutual
understanding and design your program around these
worker desires.

1. Desire for recognition, causing a person to seek
    experience in which there is social approval,
    commendation, and prestige; and to avoid exper-
    iences that result in ridicule, scorn, and
    disapproval.

2. Desire for affection, causing a person to seek
    experience involving appreciation, understanding,
    intimacy, and support; and to avoid situations
    where there is a lack of love and appreciation.

3. Desire for power, causing the person to seek
    experiences that hold promise of achievement,
    self-determination, and mastery; and to avoid
    situations involving frustration and a sense
    of failure.

4. Desire for new experience, causing a person to seek
    experiences that provide novelty, adventure, thrill,
    excitement, and change; and to avoid situations of
    dullness, monotony, and boredom.

5. Desire for security, causing a person to seek
    experiences that give assurance of protection,
    being wanted, and confidence; and to avoid
    situations involving danger, insecurity, and
    fear.

Recycling Newspaper protects more than trees.

Publicizing
Your Neighborhood
Recycling Center

        Setting up a recycling program is one thing; getting
the local residents into the habit of using it is another.
Even if the only contributors at first are those few hands-
full of people who were active in organizing the program,
and even if they advertise the center only by word of mouth,
you can expect a few hundred pounds of recyclables the
first time, and approximately a 1% increase each time you
collect thereafter. But such a relatively small volume
would make for an inefficient and disappointing venture,
especially if you plan to keep the center open several
hours per day and several days per week. It will take far
more than a few hundred pounds on each collection day to
have a "successful" operation, one that has a meaningful
impact on the solid waste and resource depletion problems.

        Begin publicizing your recycling center at least six
weeks before you cut the ribbon to its entrance. Contact
the local newspapers and radio and television stations.
Advertise your program in village, church, school, and
civic club newsletters. Make use of store, church, and
school bulletin boards. Have bumper stickers and posters
printed up, etc. Radio and television stations will usually
be happy to air your brief message as a public service
announcement and they may even be willing to air it once
or twice a week for a period of several weeks. Inform the
Mayor, City Council, and Chamber of Commerce about your
recycling project. They will be interested in the extent

to which your efforts are reducing their solid waste disposal problem, and they can offer assistance in publicizing your operation and assuring its success.[27]

Many recycling program coordinators find it useful and profitable in the early going to prepare a _BROCHURE_ for distribution throughout the community. Brochures and flyers explaining all aspects of your program can be printed up relatively inexpensively, or a local printer may be willing to donate his services.

An easily recognizable and reproducible _LOGO_ should be designed as a permanent program symbol. This logo should appear on all of your publicity announcements, publications, signs, posters, and collection equipment.

WALL POSTERS can be used to "blitz" your neighborhood or community to announce the opening of your project. They are also a highly visual and inexpensive way to remind the community of what materials you accept and where your recycling center is located. They should be visually attractive with as little written copy as possible. The who, what, when, where, and why format along with the program logo or symbol is most effective.

CALENDARS announcing where your center is, when you are open, and how to properly prepare materials are helpful and inexpensive reminders for the household. Once sheet of paper will suffice for a calendar which will alert the household recycler to your recycling days for an entire year.

Contact the _WELCOME WAGON_ or _COMMUNITY HOSTESS_ organizations or your local real estate agencies to see if they will include information about your recycling center in the information packets which they provide for new residents and homeowners.

List your recycling center in the _YELLOW PAGES_ under "Recycling."

PUBLIC UTILITIES are often willing to include notices from public service groups in their billings. _BANKS_ and _SAVINGS AND LOANS_ may include similar information in mailings to their customers. Contact each in your community regarding their mailing policies.

If you live in an area with a large population of _MINORITY GROUPS_, you should publish your posters and other information in their respective languages.

Specifically in Illinois, don't forget to *REGISTER* your recycling project with the Illinois Department of Energy and Natural Resources (309 W. Washington, Chicago IL 60606) and the Illinois Association of Recycling Centers (P.O. Box 48761, Chicago IL 60648). Each has systems available to refer people to you. Believe it or not, many environmentally-aware individuals are looking for a recycling depot to utilize or to volunteer services. Your project may be just what they are looking for.[28]

A *TIMETABLE* of collection days and hours should appear at the entrance to your recycling center. A sign telling donors exactly what items are currently being accepted and what items are not accepted should also be prominently displayed. It is a good idea to make the sign in such a way that items which are sometimes taken, other times not, can be easily switched from one category to the other on the sign. And, finally, a sign outlining preparation of materials for recycling should be prominently displayed inside the center for the benefit of both workers and the public.

Certain recycling centers have found it beneficial to focus public attention on their facility by coupling its opening -- or continuous operation -- with some sort of school or civic event. This might involve a litter cleanup campaign in the neighborhood, a shopping center rally, a recycling contest (complete with prizes), or a school contest. One of the best ideas is to hold an event such as a concert, dance, sports event, or picnic, or to show an environmentally-related film with the price of admission being so many pounds of recyclables.[29]

Whatever form your publicity takes, it should include the following information:

1. The name of your recycling center/organization

2. Who is sponsoring it

3. The names of cooperating public and private organizations

4. Why the program is important

5. Where the recycling center is located

6. Materials being collected

7. How materials are to be prepared

8. Days and hours of collection

9. Your logo

10. A phone number for people desiring further information to call

News Releases

Recognizing possible news is one of the most important parts of a publicity program. Newspapers and reporters look to you to provide them with accurate information and tips on possible stories about your program.

When releasing news about your organization's activities, remember your purpose: to give information of interest to the reader. The information should answer the basic five "W's" -- *Who, What, When, Where, and Why?* Add to this the *"How?"* which is very necessary when instructions are vital.

In general, the following guidelines may be helpful in developing news releases and feature stories:

MEET PUBLICATION DEADLINES. Become familiar with your community paper's production schedule. When does it go to press? Generally a news release announcing an event to take place on a certain date should be on the editor's desk three weeks before the intended publication date. The item may be published sooner, but this is at the editor's discretion. Photos and feature stories following an event usually have a flexible release date, i.e., for release anytime. But they should be sent out promptly after the activity takes place.

IS YOUR MATERIAL USABLE? Newspapers are partly a community service and therefore are interested in news dealing with people and groups within their circulation area. However, an editor is under no obligation to use anything sent on an unsolicited basis.

Some reasons for rejecting releases may include incomplete information, lack of identification, no news value, fuzzy photographs or a poorly-written release. Lack of space or a missed deadline may also reject a release. But by observing deadlines, writing clearly with complete information given, typing neatly, you increase your chances of getting your release into print.

TYPING/FORMAT. Type all information on one side of size 8½ x 11 paper. Do not use carbon paper or onion skin paper. Clear Xerox copies are acceptable. Double space and start the release or article at least three inches from the top of the paper page. Use your letterhead including your logo. Allow one-inch margins at the sides and bottom of the page. Use standard upper and lower case type -- do not use all capital letters, and do not underline words for emphasis.

IDENTIFY A CONTACT FOR MORE INFORMATION. At the right
of the release date, include the name of your organization
and your name and telephone number for daytime contact.

   WRITING. Don't attempt to spice a feature or news
release with adjectives; keep it simple, concise and
straightforward. Use the "inverted pyramid" format by
putting the most important information at the beginning.
An editor usually cuts from the bottom when an article
needs to be shortened. Remember the five W's: who,
what, when, where, and why. Keep your writing and editing
tight -- never run a news release to two pages when one will
do.

SAMPLE NEWS RELEASE

North Shore Ecology Center
683 Euclid, Highland Park, IL 60035
312 432-6201

PRESS RELEASE   CONTACT:
FOR IMMEDIATE PUBLICATION   GEORGE BRABEC
March 16, 1982   470-0242

              Ecology Center Recycles Record Amount
                   of Glass During February

        The North Shore Ecology Center, a State of Illinois non-profit

organization operating ten recycling centers throughout the North

Shore area, recycled a record 156.58 tons of glass or 313,160

pounds during the month of February. Prior to this record-breaking

figure, their highest monthly collection for 1981 was in October

when they collected 122.25 tons or 244,500 pounds of glass for

recycling.

        The Ecology Center, which operates in cooperation with most

North Shore communities including Lake Forest, Highland Park,

Highwood, Northbrook, Deerfield, Winnetka, Glencoe, Skokie, Morton

Grove, Niles and Lincolnwood, accepts old bottles, cans and

newspaper for recycling -- a worthwhile alternative to throwing

them into area landfills. The Ecology Center operates ten

drop-off locations which are open 24 hours each day, year 'round.

For more information on location or material preparation, call a

participating municipality or the North Shore Ecology Center at

              432-6201

              •   •   •   •   •

recycled paper

67

Pictures

As the old saying goes: "A picture is worth a thousand works," and indeed every story is better when it has a picture along with it. In order to have good pictures though, you do not necessarily have to be an ace photographer or use a fancy complicated camera. Almost any instamatic camera will give you a good photo, and with a little practice, anybody could use one. Many newspapers also will use photos that come from Polaroid cameras. Here are some tips for getting good pictures that will be usable.

* Newspapers use glossy prints which should be at least 5 by 7 inches. Do not send mats or metal for picture reproduction without first asking the editor.

* Newspapers use black and white photographs only.

* Do not crowd too many people in one picture, and do not spread them out. Unless the newspaper has specifically said that it can use a three or four column picture, take only two or three people in a picture and let them be close together. Shoulders should be touching or overlapped. This way, the picture can be used in two columns if necessary.

* In setting up the picture, keep an eye out for details. See that skirts are down, hair is in place, and that heads are not against backgrounds that would give a strange effect.

* Do not tape or staple anything to a photo.

* Do not write on the back of the photo with anything that will show through -- like the indentation of a ball point pen or magic marker that might bleed through to the faces on the front.

On-Air Exposure: Television and Radio

What is a public service announcement? A public
service announcement or *PSA* is like a television or
radio commercial. However, instead of selling a product, its message is designed to promote and publicize
an activity, event, or service of a qualified, nonprofit
organization. By broadcasting PSA's, television and
radio stations serve the entire community because, in
effect, they are broadcasting important messages and
information addressing community-wide concerns and are
making viewers aware of resources available to them.

SAMPLE PUBLIC SERVICE ANNOUNCEMENT

North Shore Ecology Center
683 Euclid, Highland Park, IL 60035
312 432-6201

Public Service Announcement   Contact Person: George Brabec
For Immediate Broadcast   470-0242

SAVING ENERGY'S A GAS

Recycling is good for your community and America.
Every ton of aluminum reused eliminates the need for
48 barrels of imported oil. Take that Opec! Be good
to your environment. For information about the recycling
center nearest to your home, call the North Shore Ecology
Center at 432-6201. That's the North Shore Ecology
Center, 432-6201. And remember, saving energy's a gas!

Dear Public Service Director:

The North Shore Ecology Center is a nonprofit, tax-
exempt community recycling program. We would be grateful
if you would broadcast the above announcement. Thank you
for your interest and cooperation.

Sincerely,

George Brabec

recycled paper

69

There are several key questions you should consider before contacting local radio and TV stations with your PSA's. What is your message? What is the basic idea you want to get across? Who should receive your message? Is it of general interest? How can you best put your message across? Does it have enough general interest for a special program or would a brief announcement such as a PSA serve just as well?

There are several ways to get air time beyond the PSA:

* Local interview shows

* Personality Spots: Announcements by on-the-air person-alities such as disc jockeys, well-known volunteers, etc.

* News Items: Short stories which are included in regular local newscasts and give briefly the who, what, when, where, and why of a newsworthy event

* Editorials: Statements prepared at the station which present the station management's viewpoint on community programs and projects

* Editorial Rebuttals: Statements prepared and presented by your organization's representative in rebuttal to a station's editorial

Public Affairs Programming

To promote your recycling program's activities, you can often take advantage of public affairs programming on radio and television stations which include the inter-view shows, local talk programs, and call-in formats.

-- Let the Program Director or Public Affairs Person know what you wish to accomplish. Let them advise you as to how to get coverage. Don't assume that your "cause" warrents News, Editorial, or Special Programming.

-- It is a misconception that a half-hour radio broadcast is always good publicity for your project. Ask your-self how many times you have sat still for a half-hour to listen to a public service program on radio, even for a five-minute program. Remember, the Program or Public Affairs Person is being paid to know what pro-gramming will gather the most audience. If you are told one 10-second announcement during prime time is more valuable than a half-hour program Sunday morning at 5:00 a.m., you can believe it.

70

When you call the stations to discuss possible programming, be prepared to submit specific facts and
workable ideas.

Please don't beg or threaten in an attempt to get
air time. A good presentation in the public interest
will stand on its own merits.

For special announcements, interviews, editorials, etc
submit all program copy as far in advance as possible.
And don't submit copy that is scribbled on scratch
paper or written in long hand.

Don't use onion skin paper for on-the-air copy.
It rattles.

Get news releases to the stations as early as possible
They can be put in their future's files for the day
they need it.

To get television news coverage, call the News Assignment Editors the day before the event to remind them
that your group's activity is happening and that they
have already received information on it from you.
Again offer an invitation and encouragement for them
to cover the affair.

When you have arranged an interview or an on-the-air
appearance, choose your organization's best representative, a person with a good voice, with enthusiasm,
who knows the subject. Be sure the date and hours
of appearances are clearly understood.

Provide a biographical sketch of any person to be
interviewed, along with a number of suggested points
to be covered. If the name is difficult to pro-
nounce, give the phonetic spelling.

For coverage on radio or TV news, send releases in
as early as possible and again call the news director
the day before the event to remind him and encourage
their coverage.

Most radio stations do not have enough personnel to
send out a reporter to cover your event, but they
will welcome a call-in from a knowledgeable person
from your organization with a statement on what
happened at the event. When you call the day before,
ask if they would like a call-in if they can't send
someone out.

Communicating to the Media

The following twelve basic "B's" for publicity will help you communicate your ideas to media representatives more effectively.

1. *BE THE ONLY PERSON* from your group to contact news media. Two members calling the same newspaper editor or program director are bound to bring conflict or confusion.

2. *BE QUICK* to establish personal contact with the right persons at each newspaper, radio and television station in your area.

3. *BE SURE* to write everything down. Train your memory, but don't trust it.

4. *BE PROMPT* in meeting deadlines.

5. *BE LEGIBLE.* Type all communications with the media.

6. *BE ACCURATE.* Double check dates, names, and places before you submit your copy.

7. *BE HONEST AND IMPARTIAL.* Give credit where due.

8. *BE BRIEF.* Newspaper space and air time are costly.

9. *BE BRAVE.* Don't be afraid to suggest something new if you honestly believe you have a workable idea. Media people welcome original ideas when they're practical and organized.

10. *BE BUSINESS-LIKE.* Never try to obtain publicity by pressure of friendship or business connections. Never ask when a story will appear. Never ask for clippings.

11. *BE APPRECIATIVE* of all space and time given your organization's publicity. The media giving it also have space and air time for sale.

12. *BE PROFESSIONAL.* Members of the press are always invited guests. Never ask them to buy tickets or pay admission. Arrange a special "Press Table" for large banquets.

<u>Informing The</u>

<u>Environmentally-Conscious Public</u>

Visits to your recycling center by the public are ideal opportunities for increasing their awareness of the beauties of nature and current environmental problems and for informing the public concerning what individuals can do to help. So keep on hand at the center copies of any such literature you may be able to obtain. Organizations listed in the appendix are excellent sources for such literature.

It is also a good idea to have your workers well informed as to the whys and wherefores of what you are doing. For example, your donors may want to know why all metal must be removed from glass before recycling. The answer is that some of the metal will end up in newly-made bottles and jars, and will often cause stress points which facilitate breaking -- or even exploding in the case of a sodapop bottle. Another question which is frequently asked is why plate glass cannot be taken. It can be recycled, however not for use in making new bottles and jars, since the lead content of plate glass is too high for these products.

Another oft-asked question is: What is the use of recycled "tin" cans? About 8% of the copper we use each year is gotten from low grade ore by "leaching" with sulfuric acid. The resulting solution is mixed with ferrous scrap leaving a copper precipitate. The copper industry currently uses almost 300,000 tons of steel cans yearly for this purpose, and demand for "tin" cans is expected to rise even further in the near future. The tin in cans is not wasted, as it is removed before their use in copper extraction.

It should be clear that a recycling center can provide more than just a place where materials are dropped off until the volumes warrent a trip to market. Answering your donors' questions will be easier if your project is staffed, but your opportunities for consciousness-raising and education are only as limited as your imagination. One Illinois program sends a monthly news release to community newspapers. Each release will address a specific recycling-education issue such as those mentioned above coupled with basic project information such as hours of operation, location, and materials collected. In this way, the project remains constantly in the public eye while providing a valuable serve in public education.

<u>Speaking Out With A</u>

<u>Speakers Bureau</u>

A speakers bureau is a great way to serve your
community while increasing your project's visibility
and effectiveness. A well-presented speech can raise
the public's consciousness -- or conscience -- about
recycling and solid waste management issues and gain
recognition for your organization as an authority on
the subject.

Press coverage of the speech can get the message
to people beyond the immediate audience. As a ripple
effect of the public support and visibility you generate, it will be easier to convince potential participants
in your program that your hard work deserves their support.

First, you will have to write a speech, develop visual
aids, and find individuals among those in your group who
would be effective on the podium. *"Speaking Out: Setting
Up a Speakers Bureau,"* published by the U.S. League of
Women Voters (Pub. No. 299, 15¢, 1730 M St., N.W.,
Washington D.C.) is an outstanding resource offering
detailed guidance in these areas.

Once you have ascertained that you have something to
say and people to say it, it's time to use a little imagination and some analysis of your community's composition,
and needs will turn up a surprisingly long list of potential audiences.

* What organizations, school associations, business groups,
  fraternal clubs, other citizens groups have meetings
  that could use a speaker?

* What groups are dealing with issues that might be affected
  by your organization's views?

* What conventions, seminars, workshops, or government
  officials could your group address?

* What classes might welcome your services in elementary
  and high schools, universities, libraries, and civic
  centers?

Brainstorming about all of the people potentially
affected by issues on which your organization has a
position will probably yield names of additional organizations. Use such sources as your local Chamber of
Commerce directory in doing your research, and be sure
to ask for, and follow up on, tips from spouses and
friends.

Final Notes on Publicity

Regardless of your chosen methods of publicity, do not stop with your initial efforts. Continue a balanced program of publicity for as long as your center is in operation. And if, for any reason, the recycling center will be closed for a period of time, be sure to have that fact well publicized at the center and through your outside contacts. This is a simple courtesy which may also prevent a junk pile from accumulating outside the closed recycling center. Finally, always be sure to publicly credit, personally thank, and keep up to date on the recycling center's progress, the individuals, organizations, and business firms that have contributed to your project's success.

If you want to leave a lasting impression on the public, then your efforts must be well timed, well planned, and well organized. While this may be a tall order to fill, particularly since you're bound to have other responsibilities and distractions during any publicity campaign, careful planning often brings very satisfying results. If you undertake a well planned publicity campaign to reach the public, you're likely to find that not only have you made an impact on the public but you've gained more friends for your organization. And just as important, you've demonstrated that public relations can be a very positive tool for action!

Because skilled use of publicity is so crucial to the success of your project, the Illinois Association of Recycling Centers maintains a file of public relations materials used by existing, ongoing Illinois programs. You may contact the organization at P.O. Box 48761, Chicago IL 60648, to make arrangements to reveiw these reference materials, or turn to this manual's Appendix II for some samples.

Your Legal Status

On pages 51-52 of this guide, legal requirements as they pertain to the operation of your recycling facility were discussed. In this section, emphasis will be placed on the legal status of your project.

As the idea of your recycling organization is introduced to your community, the group will gradually involve more people and expand its activities. As the organization grows, you will find that you need to make more decisions and do more work. Unless you want your group to remain a small discussion group, you will need to consider how to create a structure to get the work done in a way that is both fair and effective. Even a small organization needs to decide who will make decisions and how to divide the work.

Most groups begin with an informal structure that develops naturally from meeting to meeting. The people who are the natural leaders will propose ideas, choose people to help, and begin working in loose committees.

A few people who have the most ime and commitment will
do most of the work and make most of the decisions. As
the work load expands, they will discover that they want
a more formal structure for their organization in order
to get more accomplished. The larger the organization
and the more ambitious its goals, the more important it
is for the group to choose a structure for the organization.

A structure is a means to an end. It is a planned,
conscious effort to create a system so that each person
can participate fully in the organization, e-ery part of
the group performs effectively, and the leadership is
responsible to the people involved. A structure guaran-
tees that the organization will be flexible enough to
involve many different people, encourage each person's
growth, permit a variety of activities, and still remain
true to the philosophy and vision of the founders.

Take several meetings to talk about the structure
that will make your organization work best. After you
decide on a structure, test it. Try the system out for
three months or more.

Bylaws

Once you have chosen a structure, tried it out, and
decided it will work well for your group, you can write
your bylaws. The bylaws contain the "*rules of governing
the internal affairs of the organization.*" Some organizations also call their bylaws their CONSTITUTION. Whatever
you call them, take time to think about them and write
them down for three reasons.

The bylaws will tell everyone in the group what the
rules are and what each person is expected to do. They
will set a standard for future officers so that they will
be expected to work the way the founders did. Finally,
the federal government requires a signed copy of bylaws
as part of your application for tax-exemption.

The bylaws also will affect how much control you
personally retain. Because you are investing time, money,
and emotion in starting this organization, you may want
to guarantee certain responsibilities for yourself or some
one else. The fairest and safest way to write bylaws is
to discuss frankly each person's interest and how to
combine those interests with responsibility to the organization as a whole.

Bylaws create a fair system to define the power of the first officers and to transfer that power in an orderly fashion to future officers. It is perfectly alright for you to say that you want a certain office of that you hope to see the group organized in a certain way. The bylaws will be better if each person says honestly what he or she wants for himself or herself and the entire organization.

What Goes Into Bylaws?

The Citizens Information Service of Illinois (67 East Madison Street, Chicago IL 60603) publishes *The Whys, Whats, and Whos of Bylaws*, which includes the following questions you should ask yourselves when you write your bylaws.

1. What is the full, official name of the organization?

2. What is the purpose of the organization?

3. Who can become members of the organization?

4. What dues, if any, must be paid?

5. When will meetings be held, and how often?

6. How many members must be present for business to be done?

7. What officers will be necessary, how shall they be chose, and how long shall they serve?

8. What are the duties of the officers?

9. When will elections be held?

10. How shall committees be chosen?

11. How can the bylaws be changed?

How to Get Sample Bylaws

Ask similar nonprofit organizations for a copy of their bylaws. If you are part of or want to be part of a national association, the national office may be able to provide sample bylaws.

Making It Final

As you discuss what you want, write the points down. Try to keep them as short and simple as possible. Now ask a lawyer to review what you have done to make sure that the language meets the current federal, state, and local laws. Include a way to amend the bylaws as necessary. Good bylaws will stand the test of time, but also may be improved by amendments.

After everything is down on paper, send copies to everyone in your organization. After final changes, your group can vote to approve or ratify the bylaws.[30]

Should Your Group Become A

Tax-Exempt, Nonprofit Organization?

As your group defines the purpose of the organization and sets its goals, you soon will have to consider creating a legal framework for the group -- that is, you may want to incorporate. If you are only a small group of individuals, each of whom pays his or her own expenses, and you have no desire to grow, you probably do not need to incorporate. However, once you plan an ambitious program that will require handling large amounts of money and involve large numbers of people, you will benefit from doing the work necessary to convert your group into a tax-exempt, nonprofit corporation.

Forming a Nonprofit Corporation in Illinois

Forming a nonprofit corporation can be a complicated procedure. Here we hope to: 1) assist you with filing the Articles of Incorporation; 2) point out decisions you must make and government agencies you must contact; and 3) make you aware of your legal duties after incorporation.

Some of the terminology used and requirements listed may be new to you. You may want to seek the advice of a lawyer to explain these things and to outline your legal obligations at various stages of the organizing process.

These pages age offered as a basic guide only and are not meant to substitute for professional legal advice. We have attempted to be thorough and accurate but cannot be responsible for changes in state or federal laws and their application to your organization's individual circumstances and needs.

Begin by obtaining the following documents from the agencies listed.

----

* *"Not-For-Profit Corporation Guide"*
* *"General Not-For-Profit Corporation Act, 1981"*
* *Form NP-29, "Articles of Incorporation"*

Request these documents from:

ILLINOIS SECRETARY OF STATE	or	ILLINOIS SECRETARY OF STATE
Corporation Department		Corporation Department
Centennial Building		188 West Randolph
Third Floor		Room 1625
Springfield, IL 62757		Chicago, IL 60601
(217) 782-7880		(312) 793-3380

----

* *"Illinois Charitable Organization Laws"*

Request this document from:

ILLINOIS ATTORNEY GENERAL	or	ILLINOIS ATTORNEY GENERAL
Division of Charitable Trust		Division of Charitable Trust
and Solicitations		and Solicitations
500 S. Second Street		188 W. Randolph, Room 1826
Springfield, IL 62706		Chicago, IL 60601
(217) 782-1090		(312) 793-2595

----

* *IRS Publication 557, "Tax-Exempt Status for Your Organization"*
* *IRS Form #1023, "Application for Recognition of Exemption Under Section 501(c)(3)"*

* IRS Form SS-4, "Application for Employer
   Identification Number"

Request these documents and forms from:

U.S. INTERNAL REVENUE SERVICE
Forms
P.O. Box 24672
Kansas City, MO 64131

Illinois Incorporation:

What are the Articles of Incorporation?

This is the legal document through which a corporation
is formed. This document is sometimes referred to as the
CHARTER. Regardless of your future tax-exempt status, you
will need to complete and submit two identical copies of
the Articles of Incorporation, form NP-29. All the questions
must be answered.

What Goes Into Articles of Incorporation?

1. Corporate Name:

    You may choose any name you want as long as it is not the same
    as, or deceptively similar to, the name of an existing Illinois
    corporation, a foreign corporation authorized to conduct affairs
    in Illinois, or a name the exclusive right to which is currently
    reserved. You can check to see if the name you wish to use is
    currently available by writing or phoning the Secretary of
    State in Springfield.

2. Registered Agent and Office:

    The purpose of requiring each corporation to maintain a registered
    agent and office in Illinois is to provide a public record of
    the name of a person upon whom service of process against the
    corporation may be made, and of the place where such person may
    be found. This person is also the one to whom official cor-
    respondence from the Secretary of State is sent.

3. Duration:

    The duration is the period of time you plan to be incorporated.
    You can state a specific number of years, or you can make it
    perpetual, allowing the corporation to remain in existence
    until you choose to dissolve it.

4. Purpose:

    The purpose is a statement of the type of function or character
    for which the corporation is formed. Illinois requires this
    statement to be a narrow or specific purpose and will not
    accept a purpose that is too broad, general, or vague.

5. Directors:

    You must have at least three directors. They do not have to
    be Illinois residents or corporation members, but you may
    require these restrictions or impose any other qualifications
    you choose. Restrictions and qualifications may be set forth
    on the Articles of Incorporation under the "Other Provisions"
    section, or you may leave restrictions and qualifications
    to be set forth in the corporate bylaws.

6. Incorporators:

    You must have at least three incorporators, each of whom must
    be a natural citizen of the United States and at least twenty-
    one years old. Only the incorporators must sign the Articles
    of Incorporation on the last page.

7. Other Provisions:

    In this section you may list any other provisions regarding the
    internal affairs of the corporation which you wish to have
    included as part of the Articles of Incorporation. These
    may include: tax-exempt status, restrictions and qualifications,
    and other regulations.

What is the Cost and How Do You File?

    To become a nonprofit corporation in Illinois, deliver
two identical copies of the Articles of Incorporation and
$50 in the form of a certified check, cashiers check, or
money order, to the Secretary of State.

    Articles of Incorporation, whether received in Chicago
or Springfield, have their final approval only in Springfield
All Articles brought in to the Chicago office are tentatively
approved there but must be forwarded to Springfield for
final action. When approved, the Secretary of State will
stamp the date of filing on both copies of the Articles of
Incorporation and return one copy along with a Certificate
of Incorporation.

What Has To Be Done After Incorporation?

Recording:

   After you receive the Certificate and Articles of Incorporation
   from the Secretary of State, you must file them with the Office
   of the Recorder of Deeds of the county in which the registered
   office of the corporation is located. This recording must be
   within fifteen days after the Secretary of State has mailed
   these items, or as soon as possible thereafter.

Federal Employer Identification Number:

   Whether your corporation will be tax-exempt or not, you should
   apply for your Federal Employer Identification Number (F.E.I.N.).
   Almost all corporations will need to have this number at some
   time. Obtain Form SS-4 from the IRS to apply for this number.

Federal Income Tax:

   Should you decide to apply for federal income tax exemption,
   you should do so after you have been incorporated and you
   have received the Certificate and Articles of Incorporation
   from the Secretary of State.

   If you do not apply for or do not receive a federal tax exemption
   you must file federal income tax returns and pay the proper tax.
   Consult the Internal Revenue Service for the time to file and
   the forms to use.

Illinois Income Tax:

   If your corporation receives a federal tax exemption, it is
   exempt from Illinois income tax. No reports need to be filed
   and no tax is due.

   If you do not apply for or do not receive a federal tax exemption
   you must file Illinois income tax returns and pay the proper tax.
   Consult the Illinois Department of Revenue, Income Tax Division
   for the time to file and the forms to use.

   *In Springfield, the Department of Revenue is located at P.O.
   Box 3545, Springfield IL 62708, phone: (toll free) 800-641-2150.
   The Chicago office is located at 160 N. LaSalle, Chicago IL 60601
   phone: 312-793-3036.*

Illinois Sales Tax:

   Some nonprofit corporations may qualify for an exemption from
   paying sales tax on goods bought for the use of the organization
   if they are formed exclusively for charitable, religious, or
   educational purposes. To find out if you qualify, send a letter
   of request to the Illinois Department of Revenue, Sales Tax
   Division.

Springfield: 1500 S. Ninth Street, Springfield IL 62708, phone (toll free) 800-641-2150. Chicago: 160 N. LaSalle Street, Rm. 715 Chicago IL 60601, phone: 312-793-3196.

Enclose photocopies of your Articles of Incorporation, bylaws, IRS exemption letter or any other document which may help in determining your status. The Department will notify you if you qualify.

If you qualify for sales tax exemption, you will be issued a letter ruling to that effect. You may not use your nonprofit registration number of F.E.I.N. to claim exemption from Illinois sales tax.

Illinois Attorney General Registration:

Certain charitable organizations must register with the Attorney General, Division of Charitable Trust and Solicitations under either or both the Illinois Charitable Trust Act or the Illinois Solicitation Act. Information and forms should be obtained from the Office of the Attorney General (Address on page 81).

Annual Reports to the Secretary of State:

ALL nonprofit corporations must file an annual report of officers and directors with the Secretary of State, the due date depending upon when the corporation was formed. The annual report will be due before the first day of the corporation's anniversary month each year. The anniversary month means the month in which the corporation was formed. Failure to file an annual report may result in involuntary dissolution of the corporation.

Annual Reports to Other Government Agencies:

The Internal Revenue Service, the Illinois Department of Revenue, and the Illinois Attorney General may require various annual returns. Whether you must file a return and which return you will use depends in part on your status as a tax-exempt or non-tax-exempt corporation. To be sure of your obligation, consult the proper agency.

Other Reports to the Secretary of State:

Any change in the corporate name, duration, or purpose will require that the Articles of Incorporation be amended, using the proper form. Also, should the corporation need to report a merger, dissolution, or reinstatement, it should use the proper form. All forms for these reports are available from the Secretary of State and should be filed when the particular event occurs.

Tax Consequences for Nonprofit Corporations

Should your organization incorporate as a nonprofit corporation and file with the Internal Revenue Service as a tax-exempt organization? Depending on your circumstances, it may be desirable to do so. To see what this is so, let us begin by examining briefly the two basic differences between "for profit" and "nonprofit" organizations and the tax consequences for each.

For profit organizations promote the return of tangible benefits to their owners, generally in the form of profits on investments.

Nonprofit organizations are "owned" by members who receive no financial return. Nonprofit organizations enjoy both special priveleges and restrictions on their operations which are designed to provide a socially desirable service without regard to profits or financial gain.

The Tax Reform Act of 1969 created two general categories of exempt organizations, (1) the private foundation, and (2) other than a private foundation, with different rules and benefits for each.

Private foundations are subject to a number of restrictions on their activities and <u>are</u> subject to certain taxes, including a tax on the failure to distribute their income at a specified level. Normally, individual donors can deduct contributions of no more than 20 percent of their adjusted gross income to a private foundation.

Publically supported organizations, on the other hand ("other than private foundations"), receive broad public support and are subject to a minimum of federal regulation. These organizations have no specific rules on the amount of surplus they can accumulate so long as it "does not become excessive." In addition to the major tax benefits enjoyed by these organizations, individual donors to them can normally deduct contributions up to 50 percent of their adjusted gross income.

Tax Benefits

The considerable tax benefits for even small organizations that qualify with the IRS as exempt organizations may be a major consideration.

State regulations vary, but Illinois imposes a 4 percent tax rate for corporations. The federal tax system applies a 22 percent normal tax rate on corporations, plus a 26 percent surtax rate on excess income over $25,000. Thus a nonexempt Illinois organization with a net income of $77,500 pays $36,800 in taxes -- an Illinois tax of $3,100 and a federal tax of $30,700 (22% x $77,500 plus 26% x $52,500).

In addition, exempt organizations under Section 501(c)(3) of the Internal Revenue Code are not now required to pay social security taxes (unless their employees and employer elect to be covered), they may not be obligated to contribute to unemployment taxes, and they usually seek additional exemptions from state sales taxes and local real estate taxes.[32]

Securing Tax Exemption

Since tax exemption is a privilege, not a right, it must be earned. The IRS is hardly renowned for its largesse, especially when it may cost the Treasury a penny or two. Surprisingly, however, the provisions of the Internal Revenue Code giving exemptions for charitable contributions and organizations are liberally construed.

The journey to the promised land begins with IRS form 1023: "Application for Recognition of Exemption Under Section 501(c)(3) of the Internal Revenue Code.

The application, accompanied by a conformed copy (one that agrees with the original and all amendments) of the organization's certificate of incorporation, constitution or bylaws, a classified statement of receipts and expenditures, and a balance sheet for the current year and three immediate prior years must be filed in duplicate with the district director for the key district in which the organization's principal office or place of business is located. Approved applications will be made available for public inspection and copying.

If the application is accepted, a determination or ruling letter will be issued to the organizaiton. An adverse determination letter may be appealed within thirty days to the regional director of appeals.[33]

Business Management

"The entrepreneur himself doesn't come as a fullblown system. It takes a certain kind of person to get the idea and to transform it somehow or other into an implementation or a form or product. It takes another person to manage and grow it."

Running a successful recycling center calls for a great deal of ability. It is a talent, often like juggling oranges. The techniques can be learned, and the skills necessary for success can be acquired. This section deals with effective management tools for controlling the operation of your project.

What Is Management?

In general, management responsibilities fall into four groups of processes:

* Planning
* Organizing the physical aspects or resources of a business
* Organizing the "human resources" of the business
* Supervising the use of these physical and human resources

These processes are common to management in all businesses although naturally the specifics vary with the type of business. The key to successful management lies more in knowing how to apply these processes generally than it does in knowing specifically everything that is going on at any particular time.

Of course, as a recycling entrepreneur, you should be familiar with every job in your project, but knowing how the program operates does not mean you should involve yourself in the details of every job, except to those which you can bring your own expert skills and knowledge. Delegating the other jobs and concentrating on the proper management of the entire operation is the profitable course.

Even before your recycling project is underway, you are faced with an endless number of things to do, choices to make, and plans to execute. Managing a recycling center is a continuing task that is never fully accomplished, a process of constant change and continual updating. In an active organization, nothing remains the same for very long; it is management's job to meet changing conditions as well as to initiate change within the organization.

Above all, you should keep in mind that management is more than administration, although it includes administration. Management entails leadership, and the manager of any community project must display a great deal of this trait. Peers, employees and volunteers, donors, market representatives, and the community you serve must all feel confidence in the management's leadership of your program if it is to succeed.

SO MANAGEMENT CALLS FOR:

* Decision making and problem-solving skills;

* Skills in communication and human interaction; and

* Imagination, toughness, and sensitivity to the needs of others

MANAGING ENTAILS:

* Understanding and maintaining financial records;

* Monitoring of inventory and staffing levels;

* Shopping wisely for materials, tools, and equipment; and

* Administering other operations of the organization.

Planning

The first management job is planning, a combination of realistic calculations and crystal ball gazing. It is an exercise in arithmetic and imagination, in separating the possible from the impossible.

Planning consists of first setting a target or an objective for yourself, your organization, and its operations. Then you must determine the best (or at least a cost-effective) way of achieving your plan, using a step-by-step procedure. Your plan should include what people, money, space, equipment and materials are needed, when they are needed and for how long, to reach your objective.

Wise planners take a somewhat conservative view of what is realistic when estimating what can be accomplished with any given level of staff and other resources. It is a disasterous mistake to assume that everything will go according to an ideal use of these resources, with no allowance for breakdowns of machinery, delayed deliveries, sickness and other disturbances of the perfect plan. You must build in a generous contingency factor in any plan -- slippage is part of the human condition.

When you have worked out a realistic plan with conservative assumptions to achieve a given objective, you may find that you just do not have the resources, human or physical, to attain that objective. Or you may find that the process you have selected is too expensive to make business sense.

In that case you can lower your sights or try to find more resources or another approach to attaining your objective.

> *"If you don't number your transactions, someone else may number your days."*
>
>   *... Old CPA Proverb*

Accounting For Your Project

Let's be honest. For most people, accounting is boring. Particularly for people engrossed in such heady activities as changing society or helping people, balancing books and preparing financial statements seems far less important than delivering services and developing position statements.

After all, the most important thing about money is getting it, isn't it? Well, you certainly can't do much without money. But if you don't do certain things after you get it, you might not get any more.

Proper accounting can increase the confidence of your organization's constituency, including donors, community supporters, and funding sources. It can foster an attitude of professionalism that can permeate an organization and improve all of its activities. In a more abstract sense, it can do much to eliminate abuses in a field that is critically dependent on the confidence and support of the public.

Nonprofit accounting is both like and different from commercial accounting. Some of the ways are revealed in a list of functions the nonprofit accounting system is expected to serve:

INTERNALLY, THE SYSTEM SHOULD PROVIDE:

* Fiscal data on which to base budgets and other planning decisions

* An accurate record of incoming money and in-kind contributions

* Continuous recording and control of expenditures

* Periodic comparisons of actual income and expenditures with budgeted expectations, broken down into budget categories

* Cost information for program evaluation

So far it sounds very much like the accounting needs of
a business, but there is another dimension.

EXTERNALLY, THE NONPROFIT ACCOUNTING SYSTEM SHOULD
MEET THE REQUIREMENTS OF:

* Major funding sources

* Individual and corporate contributors

* Government regulatory and tax bodies

* The public (for documentation of the stewardship --
   the safeguarding and effective use of tax-exempt funds)

It is mainly the external accountability requirements
that make nonprofit accounting different. While commercial
entities are oriented toward profits, nonprofit organizations
are concerned primarily with effective programming. While
commercial accounting tries to show maximum profit for
stockholders, nonprofit accounting must satisfy outsiders
that the money entrusted to the organization has been properly
spent.[34]

Where to Get Help

In deciding what kind of an accounting system is needed
and in setting it up, most organizations should have the help
of an accountant. Moreover, if the organization receives
funds whose use is restricted by the donor, if it operates
several programs or owns a building or other extensive capital
assets, the accountant should be familiar with nonprofit fund
accounting.

If you can see your way to pay for the services of a
skilled accountant, by all means do so. Having the accountant
on your payroll gives leaverage which cannot be obtained in
any other way. A relationship on a fee basis is the best
guarantee that all parties will have a sense of responsibility
and commitment to one another.

Many groups, of course, cannot afford the fees of professional accountants. In this case, there are several possible
recourses.

Your greatest windfall would be donated help from a local
certified public accountant. National CPA firms are especially
good prospects. Because they have a larger overall volume of
business and many branch offices, they can afford to donate
time to charities as a public relations device. Do not be
afraid to ask these firms for help. Probably you will be
pleasantly surprised.

Many times the local chapters of the state CPA societies will help by asking members to donate time and assistance on a rotation basis. If you cannot get help for free from a CPA, contact a PA (public accountant) or a reputable bookkeeping firm.

You might also consider approaching one of the large business corporations in your community. Pick a firm that hires a large number of local people so that the company feels it has a stake in winning favor with the local community. Remind the firm that it is not at all unusual for companies to donate a few hours of time to local charities; it is done already in many places throughout the U.S. Also assure the company that you will give them plenty of favorable publicity if they so desire.

Sometimes you can get accounting help from a local government office. Stay away from federal and state offices; they don't have much freedom to re-arrange the hourly patters of their workers. Concentrate on city, county, or district governments.

You can also go to local universities, colleges or high schools for help. In the business departments of these institutions there is nearly always a faculty member who teaches accounting. Perhaps he or she can be persuaded to donate time or advice to your group. Perhaps a student can take on your accounting tasks as a project for which academic credit will be given.[35]

Other Sources of Information

Nonprofit accounting is not very well represented in the literature of accounting. However, there are a number of very useful sources of information, including the following.

AICPA Audit Guides:

> The basic standards of "generally acceptable accounting principles" for nonprofit accounting are set forth in the audit guides of the American Institute of Certified Public Accountants. Although these publications are written for practicing CPA's and thus are rather technical, anyone responsible for accounting of a nonprofit corporation should nonetheless have access to a copy of the appropriate guide.

> Three audit guides are currently in force for different types of nonprofits. The one most likely to be useful to you in operating your recycling program is:

> *Audits of Voluntary Health and Welfare Organizations*, prepared by the Committee on Voluntary Health and Welfare Organizations and issued in 1974 ($4.50).

Is Your Recycling Project

Breaking Even?

Throughout this text we have emphasized planning your project with the goal of having revenues from the sale of recyclables you collect cover your operating costs. Some in the field of recycling argue that recycling centers should not have to break even because the value of the service to the community is such that a dollar loss is offset by the other less tangible environmental and social benefits.

We strongly agree with the latter part of this view. Recycling indeed offers a community many outstanding benefits which cannot be measured in dollars and cents. However, no project can run in the red indefinitely, and poor profit planning has been the demise of many a fine effort.

If revenues from material sales do not cover operating costs, an organization will find it necessary to develop an ongoing fundraising program to support the project. Raising funds for the operating costs of an ongoing project is a difficult task. One goal of most recyclers, therefore, is for the project to become financially self-sufficient. How will you know when this goal has been achieved?

One tool in determining the profitability of your recycling project once it is underway is with a *BREAKEVEN ANALYSIS*.

Breakeven analysis is an analytical technique for studying the relations among fixed costs, variable costs, and profits. If your project's costs were all variable, the problem of breakeven volume would seldom arise; but by having some variable and some fixed costs, your group will suffer losses until a given volume of collections has been reached.

Breakeven analysis is a formal profit-planning approach based on established relations between costs and revenues. It is a device for determining the point at which *income will just cover total costs*. If a recycling organization is to avoid losses, its revenues must cover all costs -- those that vary directly with production and those that do not change as production (recycling volume in this case) levels change.

Breakeven analysis is not a panacea. It's only one of the many tools available to the business decision-maker. But it's a good tool with which to begin to approach decision problems. Let us examine the breakeven analysis of one recycling organization operating multiple collection depots.

Sample Breakeven Analysis of a

Multiple Site Recycling Organization

The first step in calculating breakeven is to separate fixed costs and variable costs for a specified period of time. This has been done (table 1-1) for one calendar year.

TABLE 1-1

Fixed and Variable Costs For One Calendar Year

Fixed Costs		Variable Costs	
Administrative Wages	$ 7920	Gross Wages -- Employees	$17053
Gross Wages - Director	10000	Hauling Expense	9211
Insurance	1755	Vehicle Expense	4509
Repairs and Maintenance	1489	Gas/Fuel	2030
Advertising/Promotion	1451		
Professional Fees	1517		
Depreciation Expense	2850		
Office Expense	868		
Interest Expense	615		
Telephone	481		
Operating Supplies	173		
Postage	51		
Permits and Licenses	5		
TOTAL FIXED COSTS =	$29175	TOTAL VARIABLE COSTS =	$32803

TOTAL COSTS = $61978

There are nine categories designated for fixed costs as outlined in table 1-1. It should be noted that these figures are in real dollars, and that all extraordinary expenses have been eliminated when computation of the cost is done. For example, "Outside Services" for $8904 were not entered into the computation since this account is payment of an old debt. It should also be noted that only about 95 percent of the organization's business is recycling. The group also engages in community benefit and awareness programs for which it is very difficult to separate expenses. In conclusion, table 1-1 is fairly summatic of the year's costs.

The next step in calculating the breakeven point is to determine the quantity and nature of products recycled. The organization recycles three main materials: paper, glass, and metals. These three "products" account for about 94.6 percent of revenues with the remainder being taken in from interest and donation income.

Table 1-2 below details the total volume of recycled material for the organization and for each individual center and is further divided by material type. The total project volume for the year was approximately 6,354,200 pounds of all material types.

TABLE 1-2

Calendar Year Total Weights by Location and Material Types
(figures are represented in the thousands of pounds)

Location #	Paper Wt.	Glass Wt.	Metal Wt.	Grand Total
1	1178.0	273.0	0.0	1451.0
2	918.5	286.1	0.0	1204.6
3	856.4	170.8	133.9	1161.1
4	694.2	134.6	0.0	828.8
5	522.0	111.4	0.0	633.4
6	453.5	14.4	0.0	467.9
7	456.6	0.0	0.0	456.6
8	89.0	0.0	0.0	89.0
9	52.8	0.0	0.0	52.8
TOTAL	5230.0	990.3	133.9	6354.2

TOTAL VOLUME FOR THE YEAR = 6,354,200 pounds

Now that the quantity recycled and the fixes costs have been determined, the next step is to arrive at a figure for revenue intake per unit; that is, what price each pound of recycled material commands on the market. This is a very difficult figure at which to arrive for several reasons. First, the total figure is for three different materials: glass, paper and metals. Second, the market prices set for these materials fluctuate wildly on the commodities market.

As a result, the following method was used to arrive at a price per average pound.

1) Total Revenue for the Year............. $61999

2) Percentage of Revenue from Recycling... x 94.6%

3) Total Revenue from Recycling $58651

4) Total Pounds of Materials Recycled, One Year........6,354,200 lbs.

5) Divided by Total Revenue from Recycling ....÷ $58651

6) Average Price Per Pound of Recycled Material .... $ .00923

The next figure to be derived is the variable cost per unit of recycled material. This is calculated in much the same manner the the average price per pound of recycled material and is calculated as follows:

1) Total Variable Costs for the Year $32803
2) Divided by Total Units Recycled .... ÷ 6,354,200 lbs.
3) Variable Cost Per Unit .... $ .00516 per lb

----

In summary, the following information has been ascertained:

1) The breakeven quantity is defined as the volume of material collections at which revenue is just equal to total costs (fixed costs plus variable costs).

2) The following figures will be used in calculating the breakeven point for the organization during the calendar year we are examining.

Average Revenue Per Unit	= $ .00923/lb.	= P
Quantity Recycled for the Year	= 6,354,200 lbs.	= K
Fixed Costs for the Year	= $29,175	= FC
Variable Cost Per Unit	= $ .00516/lb.	= VC

----

3) Now the algebraic solution for breakeven is computed as follows:

$$P \times K = FC + VC + K$$
$$P \times K - VC \times K = FC$$
$$K(P - VC) = FC$$
$$K = \frac{FC}{P - VC} \quad \text{at breakeven quantity or Q}$$

4) Therefore, to arrive at a breakeven quantity in terms of total pounds of recycled material for the year, only the relevant figures need to be applied. As is:

$$Q = \frac{\$29,175}{\$ .00923/lb. - \$ .00515/lb.} = 7,168,304.6 \text{ lbs. of material}$$

98

This means that in order to breakeven with costs, the organization needed to recycle 7,168,300 pounds of materials. They fell short of this figure by approximately 814,000 pounds and therefore the organization is operating below its break-even volume. The breakeven quantity in dollars of course would be Total Costs or $61,978.

On the average per recycling center, the breakeven point is approximately 79,647 pounds of materials per year. As can be noted from table 1-2 (see page 85), only four of the nine centers are at or above this figure.

What Did The Organization Learn?

This particular organization learned that they are covering their operating costs in only four of nine recycling locations, and that the revenues received from the sale of recyclables at those four sites does not cover losses in the other five. Additional funds, perhaps in the form of donation income, would have to be sought out to cover the deficits.

The analysis identified the profitable recycling centers, indicating the organization needs to increase its promotional activities in the communites where unprofitable depots are located and implement more cost-effective materials handling strategies as well.

In addition, the group confirmed what they had believed, that paper sales yielded the largest amount of recycled volume and revenues. Because market prices for the sale of recyclable materials fluctuate dramatically, the organization will spend additional time in identifying more profitable sales markets, especially for their highest volume item, newspapers.

COLORADO COLLEGE LIBRARY
COLORADO SPRINGS
COLORADO

THIS IS AN OXYGEN FACTORY.

Conserve
trees...

Recycle
Paper!

DON'T DESTROY IT NEEDLESSLY

How To Run A Community Recycling Center

A Resource Guide to Low-Technology Recycling in Illinois

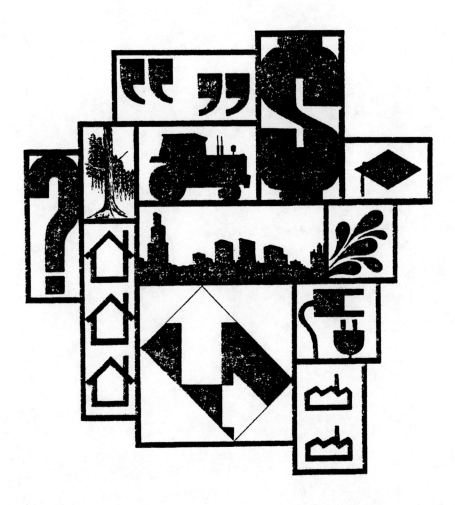

Illinois Department of
Energy and Natural Resources

Printed by Authority of the State of Illinois

RECYCLING FOCUS

NORTH SHORE ECOLOGY CENTER, INC.

THE NORTH SHORE ECOLOGY CENTER RECYCLING
SYMBOL DIRECTS PEOPLE TO RECYCLING DEPOTS
IN CHICAGO'S NORTHERN SUBURBS.

RECYCLING FOCUS

NORTH SHORE ECOLOGY CENTER

In 1971, the North Shore Ecology Center (NSEC) was incorporated
as a citizens effort to maximize the recycling of natural resources
found in our solid waste trash pile. Recycling, the planned reuse of
items normally discarded as waste, is a process offering alternatives
to present landfill disposal practices in Chicago's suburbs. The North
Shore Ecology Center recognized solid waste management as a severe
problem long before local municipalities ever thought their landfills
might run out of space.

The operation of ten recycling drop-off sites comprises NSEC's
major service to the communities of the North Shore. The depots are
available for public use in the towns of Deerfield, Glencoe, Highland
Park, Lake Forest, Northbrook, Skokie, Winnetka, and Oak Park (the first
NSEC location not on Chicago's north shore). In excess of 5000 tons
of materials (bottles, cans, and newspaper) are collected yearly at the
recycling depots which are open 24 hours daily, 7 days each week.

Additional services of the North Shore Ecology Center include:

Environmental Information and Referral Service

By calling 432-6201, citizens in the Chicago metropolitan area can
obtain information for teaching, school or club projects, business reports
speeches, homemaking, or just because they're interested. The Referral
Service helps direct people to the group, agency, or individual who can
best assist them with solutions to their environmental questions or
problems.

Environmental Awareness Programs

A slide presentation on recycling is available to organizations,
schools, and civic groups.

Energy Conservation Demonstrations

The North Shore Ecology Center offers demonstrations of a
variety of low-energy projects applying conservation technologies
Among the demonstrations offered is an electric-powered, adult
tricycle with a basket for short range, in-town errands. Also
available is a demonstration of the organization's pedal-powered
generator, an exercycle that produces electricity to operate a
small TV, radio, or tape recorder. And the NSEC also maintains a
low-energy house with solar heat featuring small size, insulation
active and passive solar heat, hot water pre-heating, and water
conservation.

For more information, write NSEC, 491 Madison,
Glencoe IL 60022.

RECYCLING FOCUS

CITY OF EVANSTON RECYCLING CENTER

EVANSTON, ILLINOIS

THIS VIEW OF THE CITY OF EVANSTON RECYCLING
CENTER HIGHLIGHTS THE NEWLY BUILT, COVERED
STORAGE FACILITY AND SPACIOUS GROUNDS FOR
RECYCLING CONVENIENCE.

RECYCLING FOCUS

CITY OF EVANSTON RECYCLING CENTER

Evanston, Illinois

In April of 1981, the Evanston Recycling Center celebrated its Grand Opening at its new location, 2222 Oakton Street in Evanston, Illinois. The City had previously operated a recycling drop-off center in their city yards. Although there is fairly strong support of recycling in the Evanston community, the city yard site had its share of problems, including vandalism and dangerous driving conditions (e.g., scattered broken glass and debris). The fact that the land was slated for sale in the near future helped promote plans for relocating the recycling center.

The idea of developing a comprehensive municipal recycling center which would incorporate the Forestry Department's handling of wood waste (as well a the recycling of cans, glass, and paper) began taking final shape in 1980. With the support of the community and the help of the City and revenue-sharing dollars, the EPA's Technical Assistance Panel, and several dedicated individuals, the Evanston Recycling Center moved to its new and larger, fenced-in location and expanded its service.

The Forestry Department assumed responsibility for the new recycling program and utilized the Environmental Internship Program to acquire a manager for the summer to organize the program, publicize it, develop a public education format, and to investigate markets. The Environmental Intern Program is a nonprofit organization which matches students in the environmental field with sponsors (either private, public, or nonprofit organizations) involved with environmentally-related projects.

The Evanston Recycling Center currently accepts newspaper, bimetal cans, clear glass, mixed brown and green glass, and recently began separating out aluminum. The Center collects a monthly average of 25 tons of paper, 12 tons of glass, 1.5 tons of bimetal, and between April and September of 1981, one ton of donated aluminum was recycled. Load lugger bins are provided by a local scrap yard and hauling company for the organization's use.

105

Since the move in 1981, the number of participants and also the level of revenues have been increasing. At one time, the Forestry Department paid over $6 per cubic yard to dump their bulky and massive quantities of cut trees in the landfill. These trees are now brought to the recycling center and used in various ways, saving dumping fees, landfill space, and a valuable resource.

Almost all Illinois communities must deal with Dutch Elm diseased trees, and contrary to popular myth, these trees can be reutilized either as wood chips for landscaping purposes, or as furniture, veneer, or as raw material for pulp and paper manufacture, to name just a few. Evanston's diseased trees are sold to be processed into lumber. The Oaks, Maples, and other hardwoods are split and sold as firewood at the Center. The limbs of the cut trees are chipped and provided free to the public, as are the stump grindings which can be used as mulch.

The wood chips, compost, and mulch serve as further incentive for those recyclers who need tangible benefits for their efforts. But more important, this wood processing operation strongly supports the recycling and waste trimming concepts that recycling centers promote.

The Evanston Recycling Center has established permanent recycling boxes in the lunchrooms and vending areas of the City Hall and Forestry Department building as one means to increase the visibility of the Center and also to encourage city employees to recycle their beverage cans. The Center plans to establish such boxes in all city buildings (e.g., police and fire departments, libraries, etc.). A similar program is also being considered with local businesses and plants.

Although recycling is definitely not new in Evanston, with the increased support and resources being offered by the City, the opportunity exists for maximizing its potential as a recycling and educational tool.

For further information, write the Recycling Manager, Forestry Department, City of Evanston, 2100 Ridge Avenue, Evanston, Illinois 60204.

RECYCLING FOCUS

THE NILES TOWNSHIP HIGH SCHOOLS
ENVIRONMENTAL RESOURCE CENTER

SKOKIE, ILLINOIS

RECYCLING FOCUS

THE NILES TOWNSHIP HIGH SCHOOLS

ENVIRONMENTAL RESOURCE CENTER

Skokie, Illinois

The Niles Township High Schools Environmental Resource Center is a project of High School District 219 encompassing the four nothern Illinois villages of Skokie, Morton Grove, Niles, and Lincolnwood. George Brabec, a graduate of Niles West High School, has managed the recycling center since its inception and is assisted by students from all three high schools in the district.

In May 1971, the reclamation program was initiated with eight waste barrels. Today, with school and community support, the program has been greatly expanded to include specialized equipment for storing and transporting materials, as well as a complete environmental resource library and community speakers bureau.

This organization is unique within the school system. No other student activity has such a regular income, nor so many responsibilities. Whereas many high school projects revolve only around the school campus, the activities of the recycling center benefit and involve the student body and the entire surrounding community.

The recycling center facilities and services are available to all, whether they are student workers or contributors of materials. The school district, citizens, government, and industry alike have contributed to the success of the reclamation center. When the recycling center appealed to industry and government for aid, support was granted.

As the project is currently recycling bottles, cans, and newspaper at a level of over 1,000 tons per year, all participants hope that this type of cooperation and participation continues because the reclamation center is providing a unique learning experience for students and community residents.

The recycling center operates not only as a symbol of environmental concern, but also as a living laboratory teaching many skills. But even more important, the recycling center serves as an illustration of what people can do, as individuals, to eliminate our solid waste problem. And in addition, the program can help modify our throw-away habits and foster a new era of respect and understanding of our environment as well as demonstrate the need for a new environmental ethic that works hand-in-hand with progress and economic development.

For more information, write the Environmental Resource Center, 7929 Austin, Skokie, Illinois 60077.

RECYCLING FOCUS

PALOS RECYCLE DEPOT

PALOS HEIGHTS, ILLINOIS

VOLUNTEERS OF THE MORAINE VALLEY COMMUNITY
COLLEGE ECOLOGY CLUB VOLUNTEER THEIR SER-
VICES AT THE PALOS RECYCLE DEPOT.

RECYCLING FOCUS

PALOS RECYCLE DEPOT

Palos Heights, Illinois

After one year of planning, the Palos Recycle Depot opened for business on Saturday, November 8, 1980. The location is part of the local Buick dealership and affords easy entry and exit, with ample room for the unloading and work area.

The Depot consists of two semi-trailers, one fixed in position without wheels and the other roadworthy. The latter is used for the newspaper, magazines, and cardboard. The fixed unit houses a 250-gallon oil tank and crushed glass. Flattened tin and aluminum cans are stored in heavy duty cardboard barrels. The materials are taken by maxi-van to market -- the exception being oil which is pumped into a tank truck.

Twelve local nonprofit organizations, representing a large variety of community concerns and causes, provide the manpower for the Palos Recycle Depot. Each works one Saturday in a quarter and receives 1/2 of the profit. After 40 weeks of operation, each organization which provided labor received $72, $129, and $158 for their efforts.

After 40 weeks of operation, collection statistics were impressive, including 3.404 lbs. of aluminum cans; 1,016 lbs. of miscellaneous aluminum; 37,369 lbs. of glass bottles and jars; 5,180 lbs. of tin cans; 500 gallons of used motor oil; and over 73 tons of newsprint, magazines, and cardboard.

Program participants feel that greater support of the project will develop as they plan a promotional campaign which will include the development of a logo and distribution of flyers to the community. Palos Recycle Depot is managed by a seven-person governing board which includes a chairman, vice-chairman, secretary, and treasurer.

For additional information write Warren Jacobek, Chairman, Palos Recycle Depot, 8011 West 124th Street, Palos Park, Illinois 60464.

RECYCLING FOCUS

MC HENRY COUNTY DEFENDERS

CRYSTAL LAKE, ILLINOIS

GLASS, CANS, ALUMINUM, AND USED MOTOR
OIL ARRIVE AT A MC HENRY RECYCLING
DRIVE.

RECYCLING FOCUS

MC HENRY COUNTY DEFENDERS

Crystal Lake, Illinois

An enthusiastic group of environmental activists initiated a glass recycling program in Crystal Lake, Illinois in February of 1971. The McHenry County Defenders, as they came to be known, have grown and prospered. Paper and tin collections were added within a year, followed shortly thereafter by the addition of aluminum. The 250-member organization now also collects used motor oil and has expanded its resource recovery programs to serve the City of McHenry, and most recently, the community of Woodstock.

The Defenders sponsor recycling drives on the third Saturday of each month. Because of the amount of labor required, the Defenders enlist the aid of a large variety of community groups. In Crystal Lake, Boy Scout Troop 127 regularly handles glass collections. For their efforts, the Scouts receive all revenues from the sale of this material. Tin and aluminum cans and used motor oil are handled by the Defenders, and proceeds from the sale of these materials supports their organization.

Proceeds for paper collections are shared by the Defenders and other community groups. The Defenders arrange for trucks, provide for insurance and publicize the drives, but labor is provided by an interested community organization. In the City of McHenry, all materials are processed by Defender members with the help of more local groups. The groups then split revenues. The Defenders believe that community involvement is the key to their program's success. Each group that participates encourages new people to recycle their bottles, cans, newspaper, and used motor oil.

Containers for the storage of glass, tin, aluminum, and used oil are provided by a local disposal company which markets the materials as well. The charge to the Defenders for the company's labor is equivalent to one half of the profits made from the glass.

Semi-trailers for collection of newspaper are usually provided by the company that purchases the Defenders' newspaper. For the past few years, paper has been sold to insulation manufacturers in the area. But the Defenders recently purchased their own semi-trailer to use in the collection of mixed paper (magazines, junk mail, etc.). A local truck driver is hired to deliver mixed paper to market.

The volume of materials recycled varies between Crystal Lake and McHenry (figures are not yet available for Woodstock). Drives in Crystal Lake serve a population of approximately 30,000; McHenry 12,000. Last year about 206 tons of paper and 480 gallons of used oil were recycled in Crystal Lake. 315 tons of paper and 410 gallons of oil were recycled in McHenry. The quantity of paper collected at the drives has decreased over the last year. Keeping track of the volume of glass and metal has been difficult because it is saved for several months and mixed with materials from other sources before it is sold.

Providing new and improved services to the community is another factor in the success of this program. Last January in Crystal Lake, the Defenders began an aluminum buy-back program in cooperation with Chicago Can Company. People have the option of selling their aluminum cans or donating them to the Defenders, who in turn sell them to Chicago Can. Hopefully this buy-back program will increase the amount of other recyclables dropped off at the drives.

In addition to the recycling programs in Crystal Lake, McHenry, and Woodstock, the Defenders have a non-roadworthy semi-trailer stationed at the Chicago & Northwestern train station in Crystal Lake. Each night, C & NW workers clean the train cars and put the newspapers they collect at this auxilliary depot.

For more information, write McHenry County Defenders, P.O. Box 603, Crystal Lake, Illinois 60014.

RECYCLING FOCUS

NAPERVILLE AREA RECYCLING CENTER

NAPERVILLE, ILLINOIS

THE NEW LOCATION FOR THE NAPERVILLE AREA
RECYCLING CENTER FEATURES A SOLAR-HEATED
SHELTER. THE RECYCLING CENTER IS LOCATED
JUST OFF OGDEN, ONE MILE WEST OF MILL ST.
THE INTERIOR CONTAINS THE CAN CRUSHER,
WORK TABLES, AND STORAGE FOR ALUMINUM.

RECYCLING FOCUS

NAPERVILLE AREA RECYCLING CENTER

Naperville, Illinois

The Naperville Area Recycling Center, locally known at NARC, is the rebirth under new auspices of the former Naperville Reclamation Center, which succumbed to a combination of causes, primarily financial, in late 1979. NARC celebrated its second anniversary at the end of March, 1982, and business is booming.

The Naperville area is a strong recycling area, donating many tons annually of materials. NARC is one of only four full-service recycling centers in DuPage County (others being located in Glen Ellyn, Elmhurst, and Villa Park); it also serves residents of Kane and Will Counties. Centers in these counties are in Bolingbrook, Aurora, and St. Charles.

NARC attempts to recycle as much as possible, and in addition to the usual newspaper, glass, beverage cans, and motor oil, the Center takes cardboard, high grade papers, tin cans, old appliances, and all other metal scrap. A scrap yard in Aurora provides a container and regular pickup for the cans and other scrap. NARC recently purchased a three-section, roofed roll-off container for glass. Paper companies provide trailers and hauling. NARC owns a small can crusher that reduces volume by 80% and saves workers the tedious and back-breaking hand-tamping used in the past. Funds for this crusher were donated by the board of the defunct Reclamation Center.

Manpower is a key concern of nearly all recycling centers and NARC handles the problem in the following manner. (NARC wishes to extend its thanks to the recyclers of Hazel Crest for their example.)

Various community organizations field teams of workers who share the task of manning the Center on a rotating basis. Saturday teams work an 8-week rotation; Wednesday teams alternate every 4 weeks. Unaffiliated volunteers supplement teams and occasionally shoulder the entire burden when an organization team is not available. Children over the age of 10 may work with an adult who knows them and will supervise them. Teen groups often assist adult groups.

At each Annual Meeting, some funds from various sales income are distributed among the volunteer organizations on a pro-rata basis, depending on how many times they have worked. Income is also spent on equipment, advertising, and lease payments to the City of Naperville.

NARC is a nonprofit 501(c)(3) organization operating on city land. Recently the recycling center moved from its old location to make way for a Sesquicentennial Park. The City provided the capital for improvements of a new site. The opportunity to move to a new location was full of excitement with many decisions to be made. When asked what they wanted most in a new center location, workers agreed, "To be warm in winter!" Thus a solar heated shelter was proposed and built.

The solar shelter is a 20' x 30' building with earth on all but the south side, utilizing a "solar attic" concept. The designing architect, Kenneth P. Woods of Naperville, will be glad to discuss his design with interested parties. Cost of construction is expected to be just over $20,000. The interior will hold the can crusher, work tables, plumbing, and storage for aluminum.

For additional information, write NARC, P.O. Box 894, Naperville, Illinois 60540.

THE RESOURCE CENTER
Chicago, Illinois

COMMUNITY RECYCLING CENTER
Champaign, Illinois

OPTIONS RECYCLING TEAM
Chicago, Illinois

Profiles of these organizations can be found in the next section, "Recycling: Possibilities for Ecolomic Development."

117

Garbage removal in the '80s:

Only for the rich?

Recycling:

Possibilities for Economic Development

BY

GREG LINDSEY

The preparation of this chapter, Recycling
Possibilities was made possible by a grant
from the Community Renewal Society, 111 N.
Wabash, Chicago IL. Questions regarding
the work of the Society in recycling may
be directed to Mr. Tom Carlson. The Dept.
of Energy and Natural Resources and the
North Shore Ecology Center appreciate the
support of the Society in this endeavor.

Recycling:

Possibilities for Economic Development

"These budget cuts are killing us."

"Yeah. We need to raise some money, and we need to find some jobs for our people. I don't know what to do -- everyone is having problems. The economy is a mess."

"Look at this place. It's a mess too. I can't believe what a dump this neighborhood is. The street's filled with garbage; cans and bottles all over."

"I heard we could sell those cans over on 39th Street."

"Where? How much?"

"Oh -- penny a can. At Options."

"What's Options?"

"It's this program that trains people for jobs. They used to run a bunch of CETA programs. One of their programs is recycling. People bring in bottles and cans and paper and they hire people with the money they get from selling the stuff."

"Hey! Maybe we could start one of those programs."

"Sounds good! There's lots of waste. If we cleaned this place up, it would look alot better. We could create jobs just like at Options. Then we wouldn't have to worry about the government cutting out its jobs programs."

"Sure! I read an article the other day where it said the potential for recycling is increasing, and that with the energy shortage and less materials, recycling will be needed more. That means business should get better . . ."

****

So, you want to recycle. And you want to improve the neighborhood. Recycling seems a natural. A recycling program would reduce waste and help clean up the neighborhood. Collecting, sorting, processing, and shipping materials is work, and work means jobs. Jobs mean money, and neighborhoods where people have jobs and money are stable. Stable neighborhoods are nice places to live.

121

But wait a second. Last year, in all of Chicago, a city of 3 million, there were only two programs that recycled cans, glass, cardboard, newspaper, used oil, and other materials. Think about it. In the second largest city in America, there are only two programs with a service approach to recycling and a commitment to providing local people with jobs. One since has folded. Sure, there are a number of aluminum buy-back programs run by private business, and there are several junk yards that will buy a variety of types of scrap. But these operations generally do not have a commitment to serving the area in which they are located, and do not try to handle all types of domestic waste. They may or may not employ people from the neighborhood. Why? Why is there such a conspicuous lack of recycling programs in the City?

The reasons are simple, at least in one sense. People with money who could invest in recycling operations simply don't because they can't earn the type of return that they could if they invested in a different enterprise. The costs of collecting, sorting, processing, and shipping materials simply are too high for individuals who are interested in recycling solely as an economic venture. So recycling exists primarily in the realm of community organizations whose leaders possess imagination, creativity and dedication but often lack the practical knowledge, the management skill, and the mechanical ability necessary to make a marginal operation successful.

Sound disappointing? Perhaps. But the optimism and idealism that permeates much of the literature about recycling needs to be tempered. Novices in the field need to know that recycling, when practiced on a daily basis on a significant scale, is a hard, dirty business. The fun and frivolity associated with an occasional recycling drive or even a regular stint with friends at a permanent recycling depot fades quickly when the volunteer service aspect ends, the program becomes a business, deadlines must be met, service contracts must be honored, prices drop and volumes increase, and laborers are expected to handle increasing volumes of waste while managers have less money with which to pay them.

But recycling can work. The Resource Center in Hyde Park is an example. So is the Community Recycling Center in Champaign. These programs are making a go of it. Their staffs substitute ingenuity and perseverance for their lack of experience, and hustle for their lack of capital. And they are successful. Their programs continue despite considerable odds. And you can learn from their experience.

This chapter includes enough information about their operations to enable you to know what you are getting into if you decide to begin a program. Its thesis is that re-cycling can work, that it can contribute to the economy of a low-income neighborhood.

It is written primarily for individuals or organizations in the Chicago area although the principles discussed herein would be relevant to programs in any low-income area. The material presented in this chapter should be used in con-junction with the previous chapters of this guide. Hopefully when you finish this chapter, you will have a better under-standing of the potential for recycling in areas where devel-opment is needed, and an accurate understanding of the difficulty inherent in establishing a program that actually makes a significant contribution to an area's economy.

The introduction to this manual presents the primary audience and purpose for this guide:

> "This guide is directed mainly to environmental clubs and organizations, scouts, church groups, schools, service clubs, and individuals who wish to earn some extra cash while performing a vital community service."

This chapter moves beyond previous chapters to discuss the potential for a recycling program to function as a business -- or at least as a program that operates within and recognizes the parameters and constraints with which businesses must contend. As such, its perspective varies somewhat from the previous chapters.

Existing Programs

When this chapter was begun, there were at least three recycling programs in Illinois with commitments to economic development in the neighborhood or community that they serve:

* the Resource Center, which serves the Hyde Park-Woodlawn neighborhoods in Chicago;

* the Community Recycling Center, which serves all of Urbana-Champaign; and

* Options, Inc., located on 39th Street in Chicago.

Now there are two.

The Resource Center was started primarily to give
residents of Hyde Park and Woodlawn opportunities to
recycle. As it has evolved, it also has embraced the
goal of providing jobs for neighborhood residents.
The Community Recycling Center was founded both to
promote ecologically sound methods of waste management
and to expand job opportunities associated with recycling
in the community, especially for those who experience
difficulty finding jobs in the open market. It has pur-
sued both of these goals actively since its inception.

Options, Inc., a job-training agency, began a recycling
program early in 1981 as one of four revenue-producing,
training programs that it administers. The recycling program ended during the preparation of this chapter, and it
is doubtful at this point that the program will be revived,
although there is a slim possibility that it could be
revived in a different form.

These programs are profiled below. Their revenues
and expenditures are reviewed to determine the extent to
which they make or made ends meet. (It is, remember,
assumed by most that recycling programs are service
programs; they do not earn profits. A self-sufficient
program, one that pays its bills without subsidies, is
extremely successful.) The number of jobs provided by
each program also is treated, and the extent to which
each program contributes to the local economy is assessed.
Finally, based on the strengths and weaknesses of each
program, some general observations are made about programs
geared toward economic development.

Resource Center

The Resource Center of Hyde Park-Woodlawn, located at 6100 S.
Blackstone in Chicago, was founded in 1969 by Ken Dunn and other
students from the University of Chicago. Dunn, who remains Director
of the program, oversees paid employees and volunteers and works closely
with a volunteer Board of Directors. The Resource Center, a nonprofit
organization, maintains a diverse program. The core of its program is
the recycling of domestic and commercial wastes, including aluminum,
bimetal, and steel (tin) cans, glass, newsprint, cardboard, high-grade
office paper and other white paper, used motor oil, and all types of
ferrous and non-ferrous scrap.

The Resource Center provides curbside collection services, operates
a buy-back program, and collects materials from businesses. Residents
also drop off materials at the Center, although this accounts for a
small percentage of its volume. Most of the materials recycled by
the Resource Center are obtained from a buy-back program operated in
a vacant lot near its main building. Materials from the curbside
program are collected in Volkswagen vans. An estimated 9,000 households participate in the program. The Center also collects materials,
mostly cardboard, from more than 30 local businesses. Used cardboard
balers have been repaired and placed in the commercial establishments.
The business, which can buy the balers if they choose to, are paid for
the baled cardboard.

In addition to its recycling programs, the Center operates a variety
of other "reuse" programs. Old clothing and household items are available free-of-charge and people can trade or borrow from a used book
library. Teaching materials and classroom supplies are available in
exchange for small quantities of recyclables. Anything that has a
potential use is saved, and barter is the preferred method of exchange.

The Center also operates or has operated a number of other programs
that are consistent with an "alternative" approach to business. The
Center's vehicles are maintained by a mechanic in exchange for use of
the Center's garage facilities. The building that houses the Resource
Center, an old bus depot purchased for $20,000, is heated partially
by solar power. A wood stove helps heat the garage area. A bicycle
repair shop has operated at the Center, a kitchen with commercial baking
ovens has been used to bake bread for sale at the clothing store and
elsewhere, and community gardens have been planted. All in all, the
Resource Center exemplifies and embraces the ideas and tenets of
"Neighborhood Technology."

If you visit the Resource Center, you will likely be impressed,
not necessarily favorably, by its chaotic appearance. But there is a
method to the madness, and there are several reasons why the mess has
accumulated. Most of the reasons pertain to the operating philosophy
of the Center. The idea that "form and style follows function" is
adhered to conscientiously, and although, practically, the program
managers have little choice. Their frugal budget has little room for
niceties, and there always are more urgent matters than sprucing up to
attend to.

Practical application of the idea that "everything has a use" means that nothing is thrown away. Saving things results in clutter, but this bothers the occasional visitor much more than the staff, who apparently are comfortable in their surroundings and know where things are located. Saving odds and ends of this and that has another advantage: the Resource Center rarely purchases parts or materials for repair of its equipment or vehicles. If the needed item isn't in stock, it usually can be fabricated from something that is.

The disorder also is a safety precaution. The Resource Center, not a secure structure, has suffered signficant losses from theft, especially of tools and equipment. An unwanted intruder, unfamiliar with the surroundings and operating in the dark, will likely be stymied by the confusion.

Another of the Resource Center's maxims is "don't buy it -- get it donated, find it, or fix an old one." The inevitable result of this policy is that a lot of equipment is in poor shape, especially aesthetically. For example, none of the semi-trailers at the buy-back site cost more than $300. Most of these items would be considered junk by a typical business, but they've found a home at the Resource Center.

The unsightliness of the Center does have adverse consequences, and the Center's image in the neighborhood is not the best. The City of Chicago forced the buy-back operation to relocate once because it allegedly attracted rats, and neighbors have argued that the Center industrializes the neighborhood. Since part of its roof collapsed under heavy snow three years ago, the Center has repeatedly been called to court to report progress toward conformance with building codes. Despite these problems, the Center endures; it offers neighborhood residents alternatives to conventional waste management practices, it employs individuals from the neighborhood, and it is a source of revenue for people who sell materials at the buy-back program.

How much waste does the Resource Center recycle? Is the volume of waste handled by the Center a significant portion of the waste stream? How many people does the Center employ? Is the Center self-sufficient? These are important questions, and the answers to them provide additional information about how the Center operates and whether it makes a significant economic contribution to the community.

The Resource Center recycles approximately 60 to 65 tons of material per week. By weight, cardboard comprises the largest percentage of materials that are recycled (Table 1). This reflects the large volume of cardboard that is collected from businesses that use balers supplied by the Resource Center. By weight, newspaper, glass, and aluminum account for slightly over 50% of the wastes recycled. These items come principally from the buy-back operation and the curbside collection program. White paper, steel, bimetal cans, scrap aluminum, and other miscellaneous items account for only 11% of the total volume.

Table 1. Materials recycled by Resource Center, 1981.
            (Based on 65 tons per week)

Recyclable Material	Tons	Percent of Total
Cardboard	1,300	38.2
Newspaper	1,040	30.5
Glass	468	13.7
Aluminum (Cans)	208	6.1
White Paper/High Grade	156	4.6
Steel	104	3.1
Bimetal	104	3.1
Scrap Aluminum	26	0.8
Miscellaneous	-	-
Total	3,406	100.0%

****

Staff at the Resource Center believe that the buy-back program is the most successful component of its entire operation because of the benefits it offers to neighborhood residents. In relatively low income areas, appeals to recycle for reasons as abstract as conservation of energy and natural resources or community improvement are not very effective. Direct monetary compensation for recycling, however, works very well, as the numbers attest. The Resource Center estimates that the buy-back operation accounts for 60% to 70% of its total volume, far more than the curbside collections or donations. In 1980-81, more than $36,000 was paid to individuals who recycled various waste materials.

The volume of waste handled by the Resource Center is significant. The City of Chicago collects waste only from residential buildings with four units of less; all other waste is collected by private scavengers. In 1979, the City collected 5,794 tons of domestic waste in Ward 5, which includes portions of Hyde Park and Woodlawn. During the same year and for the same general area, the Resource Center handled 59% as much waste as did the City. Although most of the waste in Ward 5 is generated by residents in large apartment buildings, commercial establishment, and industries and therefore is collected by private haulers, the figure is useful for comparison.

Another method of estimating the effectiveness of the Resource Center is to compare the amount of waste recycled to the amount of waste generated in Hyde Park-Woodlawn. The population of Hyde Park-Woodlawn in 1980 was 67,251. Estimates of waste generated per capita per day vary considerably and depend on whether commercial and industrial wastes are included. Although no official figures are available for Chicago, an average of 3 pounds per person per day of residential and commercial waste is useful for general planning purposes. Based on this estimate, roughly 37,000 tons of waste are generated annually in Hyde Park-Woodlawn. The Resource Center recycles approximately 9% of the waste stream. This figure compares favorably with any program in Illinois, and represents a significant contribution to solid waste management in Hyde Park-Woodlawn.

Table 2. Sources of revenues and categories of expenses
for the Resource Center, 1980-81 fiscal year

Total Revenues: $103,976   Total Expenses: $104,150
Total Volume: Approx. 3,400 tons/year

Revenue Source	Percent of Total Volume	Percent of Total Revenues	Expense Category	Percent of Total
Cardboard	38.2	23.0	Payroll-related	50.4
Newspaper	30.5	30.5	Payment for Recyclables	35.3
White Paper	4.6	0.4	Property Taxes	2.1
Bimetal	-	-	Legal Fees	1.2
Steel	5.1	4.6	Telephone	0.5
Aluminum	6.1	32.1	Repair and Maintenance	4.0
Glass	13.7	6.9	Depreciation	3.7
Scrap	0.8	(a)	Equipment losses	0.6
Miscella-neous (b)	-	2.5	Hauling	1.7
			Miscellaneous	0.5
Total	100.0	100.0	Total	100.0

(a) Included in miscellaneous
(b) Includes donations, pick-up service, wood, refunds, grant, and miscellaneous sales

****

As a business, the Resource Center pays its bills and operates without direct subsidies. The total revenues in the 1980-81 fiscal year were $103,976 (Table 2).

Most of the revenues for the Resource Center come from the buy-back program. We noted previously that 70% of the Resouce Center's volume comes from the buy-back program; this same 70% of the volume probably accounts for slightly more than 70% of the revenues. This is because of the relative values of the different materials. Aluminum, accounted for only 6.1% of the total weight of materials recycled. Sales of aluminum, however, generated 32.1% of total revenues, more than the sales of any other item. Virtually all aluminum handled at the Center comes from the buy-back operation. Newsprint, which accounted for slightly over 30% of both volume and revenues, was second in terms of gross value. Newsprint is collected through curbside collection as well as through the buy-back operation.

The figures in Table 2 indicate the relative value of all recyclables. By ton, aluminum clearly is the most valuable commodity. The values in the table, however, are gross values. These are somewhat misleading because they do not necessarily indicate net value (i.e., the gross value less the costs of collecting, handling, processing, and shipping). The Resource Center has not calculated the costs of handling recyclables on a per-item basis. Thus, the relative net values of recyclables cannot be determined. Handling costs for aluminum, however, are not greater than for other materials, and it is clear that aluminum is the most valuable component of the typical waste stream. This has implications for designing a self-sufficient program. These are discussed in subsequent sections of this chapter.

Expenditures for the Resource Center in 1980-81 totalled $104,150. Payroll-related expenditures, about one-half of total expenses, and payment for recyclables about 35% of total expenses, together accounted for more than 85% of total expenditures. This reflects the labor-intensive nature of the program and the reliance on the buy-back program to generate recyclables. The small percentages of expenditures in other categories reflects the Resource Center's policy to scavenge rather than purchase the equipment and supplies that are needed.

A comparison of revenues to expenditures indicates the Resource Center spent only $174 more than it took in. Thus, on paper, the program broke even. The ledger sheet, however, does not account for all costs. For example, volunteers contributed significant amounts of time, time crucial to the Center's operation, but time that would be expensive if the program operated as a typical business.

Other unique features about the Resource Center also are not reflected in the ledger. Most of them have to do with the dedication of the staff, especially its manager, Ken Dunn. Dunn is gifted mechanically and is able to take junk and make it work. He maintains the Center's equipment and vehicles at an extremely low cost. He also is willing to work for a fraction of what he could earn in private industry. His annual salary is $12,000, which, if averaged over his typical 7-day work week, comes to less than $4.00 per hour. Other staff are paid less. In 1980-81, the Center employed four full-time and three part-time people, in addition to Dunn. The total amount paid in wages, salaries, and related expenses was only $52,490. Thus, each person works for something close to minimum wage, without benefits. Moreover, payment of salaries and wages often is deferred if the Center's cash flow is poor. The Center's liabilities at the end of 1980-81 included over $17,000 in accrued salaries and wages. This type of dedication and commitment does not exist in a typical business -- most individuals simply are not willing to work so hard for so little material reward. Dunn himself admits that most people cannot imagine why the Center still is in business after examining its financial statement. But he insists the Center will endure and is confident it will grow stronger.

So, is the Resource Center's contribution to the neighborhood economy significant? Will this depends partially on your point of view, our response is an unqualified yes. A significant percentage of the neighborhood waste stream, perhaps as much as 9%, is recycled. Eight people have at least part-time employment, and eight people with jobs, even low-paying ones, is better than eight people without jobs. More than $36,000 was paid to local residents and businesses who recycled. Most of this money probably was recirculated throughout the neighborhood economy. While it is not a lot, it helps. And it all comes from garbage that most people throw out.

For more information, write the Resource Center, 6100 S. Blackstone Chicago IL 60637.

Community Recycling Center

The Community Recycling Center (CRC), Champaign, Illinois, was founded in 1978 by graduates of the University of Illinois, encourages recycling, and provides job training. CRC, which initially operated under the auspices of the University of Illinois YMCA, has grown rapidly during its first four years. Its program has evolved from a tiny operation in a small, vacant lot to a fairly large operation involving the collection of recyclables from seven or eight drop-off sites located throughout Champaign-Urbana, limited curbside collection service, and collection from numerous businesses that generate large quantities of materials. CRC also manages an aluminum buy-back program.

Low income individuals are given work experience at the Center. They also receive assistance in locating jobs in the private sector subsequent to their training at the center. Individuals on probation and other offenders perform community service work at the Center. In addition to paid staff and service workers, volunteers donate hundreds of hours of work annually.

CRC also is involved in educational programs and in planning for improvements in the Champaign-Urbana solid waste management system. Paper recycling programs have been started in schools and CRC staff and volunteers regularly lead educational programs for schools, churches, and other community organizations. CRC representatives also have played key roles in the activities of the Champaign-Urbana Solid Waste Litter Reduction Committee that was created by the local city governments to investigate the feasibility of recycling, litter control programs, and other methods of solving waste problems. The Committee now is making recommendations about programs to be implemented in conjunction with the development of an energy recovery facility in the community. Current proposals developed by the committee call for the imposition of a surcharge on landfill dumping fees to fund recycling and litter control programs.

The growth of the CRC is evident in its volume statistics and its financial statements (Table 3). The total volume of materials handled by the CRC has increased more than five-fold in four years. Revenues from the sales of recyclables have increased from $4,473 to $100,613, a factor of more than eighteen. Each year has witnessed a steady increase in the volume of each material recycled, with the exception of high grade paper (the volume of which has fluctuated) and mixed paper (the recycling of which is not encouraged). The tonnages of glass and newsprint, which together account for over two-thirds of the total volume recycled by weight, have quadrupled. Growth in the volume of aluminum has been spectacular. Tonnage has increased from 1.4 tons to 81.4 tons as a result of the implementation of a buy-back program.

Table 3. Sources of revenues and volume of recyclables for Community Recycling Center, 1978-1981 (a)

Sales Revenues	1978				1979			
	Volume	% of Total*	Revenues	% of Total*	Volume	% of Total	Revenues	% of Total
Glass	91.1	40.1	3,230	59.0	197.8	31.7	5,549	34.7
Newspaper	109.3	49.1	1,449	26.5	250.3	40.1	4,048	25.3
Cardboard	14.4	6.5	-(b)	-	79.9	12.8	2,293	14.4
High Grade	-	-	-	-	26.7	4.3	980	6.1
Tin	-	-	-	-	16.2	2.6	1,535(c)	9.6
Bimetal	6.35	2.9	191(c)	3.5	16.9	2.7	-	-
Aluminum	1.4	0.6	532	9.7	2.8	0.4	1,131	7.1
Scrap	-	-	-	-	-	-	-	-
Mixed Paper	-	-	-	-	33.4	5.4	-	-
Oil (gallons)	300.0	70.0	-	-	546.0	-	-	-
Refillables	-	-	-	-	-	-	317	2.0
Interest	-	-	-	-	-	-	13	0.1
Miscellaneous	-	-	-	-	-	-	112	0.7
Subsidy:								
CETA			33,995				35,614	
Other							7,150	
Total	222.6	100.0	5,473	100.0	623.9	100.0	15,978	100.0
Total with Subsidy			39,468				58,742	

* Excluding subsidy.
(a) Volume of all materials, except oil, is in tons; oil is in gallons.
(b) Included with newspaper revenues.
(c) Includes revenues for tin and bimetal.

Table 3. Sources of revenues and volume of recyclables
for Community Recycling Center, 1978-1981 (a)
(Continued)

Sales Revenues	1980				1981			
	Volume	% of Total*	Revenues	% of Total*	Volume	% of Total	Revenues	% of Total
Glass	252.0	25.4	7,570	12.9	361.4	31.0	12,863	12.8
Newspaper	425.0	42.9	10,361	17.7	453.7	38.9	6,273	6.2
Cardboard	133.0	13.4	3,556	6.1	116.8	10.0	2,559	2.5
High Grade	47.0	4.7	2,263	3.9	32.4	2.8	1,112	1.1
Tin	23.0	2.3	1,725	2.9	39.7	3.4	2,633	2.6
Bimetal	22.0	2.2	790	1.3	30.0	2.6	5,608	5.6
Aluminum	48.3(4.3)	5.3	27,841	47.6	81.4	(2.8)	55,285	54.0
Scrap	8.3	0.8	-	-	11.1	1.0	-	-
Mixed Paper	32.0	3.2	-	-	40.0	3.4	-	-
Oil (gallons)	9,931.0	-	1,490	2.5	25,242(3,000)	-	6,312	6.3
Refillables	-	-	269	0.5	-	-	206	2.2
Interest	-	-	-	-	-	-	117	0.1
Miscellaneous	-	-	2,670	4.6	-	-	7,645	6.6
Subsidy:								
CETA			91,945				83,984	
Other			8,030				8,725	
Total	990.3	100.0	58,535	100.0	1,167.4	100.0	100,613	100.0
Total with Subsidy			158,510				193,327	

* Excluding subsidy.
(a) Volume of all materials, except oil, is in tons; oil is in gallons.
(b) Included with newspaper revenues.
(c) Includes revenues for tin and bimetal.

133

It is revealing to note that the growth in revenues clearly has out-paced the growth in volume. This is primarily because the major growth has been in aluminum, the most valuable recyclable. Sales of aluminum accounted for almost 55% of total revenues from the sale of materials. Volume and revenues from the sale of used oil, the value of which recently increased, also increased significantly. An improved market for bimetal cans also contributed to increased revenues in 1981. Inflation accounted for very little of the increase in revenues, prices for many materials, especially newsprint and other paper products, decreased in 1981. The relative value of each material can be estimated by comparing the percentage of volume accounted for be each recyclable to the percentage of revenues accounted for by each recyclable. As noted earlier, this does not address the net value of each commodity. Except for aluminum, data on the amount of handling that is necessary to prepare each material for shipping are not available, and comparisons of the advantages of handling one recyclable rather than another cannot be made.

As its aluminum buy-back program has grown, the CRC has placed emphasis on managing it more effeciently. The costs of the program have been analyzed, and it is clear that revenues exceed expenditures. Aluminum is bought from the public three days a week between 9:00 a.m. and 4:00 p.m. Only one person is assigned to the buy-back operation, and he or she usually has time to help with other tasks. Aluminum is weighed on an electrical digital scale and fed through a magnetic separator-blower from which it is blown into a 40-foot semi-trailer. On a busy day, 2,500 pounds of cans may be purchased and the worker will have time for little else. CRC estimates it costs approx. 5¢ per pound for handling and hauling:

* Labor costs, based on a worker at $4.00 per hour, are between 2¢ and 3¢ per pound.

* Hauling costs are between 1.5¢ and 2¢ per pound (the market used by CRC is in Chicago, 135 miles away; 16,000 pounds of flattened cans fit into the trailer).

This does not include equipment costs. The Center is fortunate in that its flattener/blower is provided as part of its contract with its market.

The Center tries to maintain at least a 7¢ to 8¢ margin of revenues over expenditures. This means that the amount paid to the public is, at most, seven or eight cents less than the price CRC receives from its market. This ensures that the Center will make two or three cents per pound profit. For example, CRC recently was receiving 29¢ per pound for aluminum cans. The amount the Center was paying for these cans then ranged from 16¢ to 22¢ per pound, depending on the total weight of the cans purchased on the transaction. Therefore, the minimum margin was 7¢.

CRC's analysis of aluminum transactions by weight for a four month period is presented in Table 4. During this period, more than 80% of the transactions brought in less than 50% of the total weight. Because each transaction involved fixed costs (i.e., time for inter-action with the seller, preparation of a receipt, and payment by cash or check), it made sense for CRC to discourage smaller transactions. The pricing policy that was adopted discourages transactions of less than 100 pounds. Similar analyses for other recyclables would enable the Center to make its entire operation more efficient.

****

Table 4. Analysis of aluminum transactions by weight, Community Recycling Center, May-November

Pounds of Aluminum	Transactions			Weight (lbs.)		
	Total	Average Per Month	Percent of Total	Total	Average Per Month	Percent of Total
0-50	1,435	359	82.4	28,290	7,072	48.4
51-100	208	52	11.9	14,381	3,595	24.6
101-200	86	22	4.9	11,423	2,856	19.5
201-500	12	3	0.7	3,345	836	5.7
501-1000	-	-	-	-	-	-
1001-2000	1	.2	0.05	1,041	260	1.8
Total	1,742	-	100.0	58,480	-	100.0

****

Because of its analysis of its handling costs, the Center insti-tuted a pricing policy that pays greater amounts to individuals who recycle larger volumes (Table 5). This, of course, makes sense because of the economics of scale that are realized when large volumes are handled

****

Table 5. Community Recycling Center aluminum prices.

Weight (pounds)	Purchasing Price (cents)
1 to 99	16
100 to 499	17
500 to 999	19
1000 or more	22

****

Despite the recent growth in revenues from sales of materials, the Center still is heavily reliant on subsidies. Last year, 1981, is the only year that the Center's earned revenues (52% of total revenues, including subsidies) exceeded subsidies (Table 3). Most of the subsidies have been CETA grants, although local revenue sharing funds also have been awarded. CETA funds have been awarded for job training activities. Revenue sharing monies have also been given for capital improvements and equipment. The CRC also has been the recipient of small grants from ACTION (to initiate the curbside collection program) and the National Center for Appropriate Technology (to construct a glass processing system and to initiate curbside collection in a low-income area).

The award of CETA grants to the Center reflects its concern for training. These grants have been based on the Center's ability to provide meaningful work experience and training opportunities for unemployed and underemployed individuals and to assist them in finding private sector jobs following their employment with CRC. Support of CRC's recycling program as a worthwhile community endeavor has been of secondary important to CETA officials. Grants from CETA to the Center have totalled more than $245,543. The Center has trained more than 110 workers, almost two-thirds of whom subsequently found private sector employment, returned to school, or were considered positive placements for other reasons (Table 6). Just over one-third of the trainees were considered non-positive terminations. A 65% success rate is good, especially considering the difficulties inherent in working with the chronically unemployed. This is especially true for the Center, which has been regarded favorably by local CETA officials for its willingness to work with trainees who have severe problems or who have had problems at other worksites.

****

Table 6. Placement of CETA trainees by
          Community Recycling Center, 1978-81

	1978-79	1979-80	1980-81	1981 to date	Total
Total number of trainees	3	39	67	4	113
Private sector positive placements	1	12	24	2	39
Other positive placements	1	12	21	-	34
Total positive placements	2	24	45	2	73
Non-positive placements	1	15	22	2	40

136

Although the CETA subsidies have been ostensibly for job training, they have been a key to the Center's growth. Besides providing labor for the Center's programs (which are extremely labor intensive), the grants also have helped provide salaries for the Center's directors and administrative staff. Prior to receipt of the initial grant, none of the founders of the Center were paid. The CETA grants have provided small administrative salaries, between $100 and $300 per month depending on the grant and the number of workers being trained, that have enabled the Center's staff to eke out a subsistence living. Unfortunately, the situation still persists. All of the CETA participants who work for minimum wage for at least 20 hours per week earn more than the Center Director and Assistant Director. This situation cannot be expected to continue indefinitely.

As the Center's revenues and subsidies have increased, so have its expenditures. Table 7 presents expenditures by category for 1978 through 1981. Salary and wage-related items under CETA contracts have accounted for the largest percentage of expenditures, although the percent of expenditures attributable to CETA activities has declined each year. The percentages of expenditures by category differ noticeably between the years 1978 and 1979 and 1980 and 1981. This is because of the introduction of the aluminum buy-back program. Prior to initiation of the program, the Center made no payments for recyclables and was unable to pay any salaries from its earned revenues. After the program began, payment for recyclables became a major expense item. The Center also was able to pay staff for the first time. Besides CETA expenses, other salary-related expenses and payment for recyclables, other major expense items include hauling, gas and oil, vehicle maintenance, insurance, rent, and utilities.

Financially, the program has broken even. The Center also has accumulated significant assets, including several trucks and trailers, a baler, glass processing equipment, can flatteners, and a fork lift. Unfortunately, the Center's financial statements do not accurately reflect the amount of work that it actually takes to make the Center run. Literally thousands of hours of volunteer labor are expended at the Center annually.

* The Director and Assistant Director are woefully underpaid; at $250 per month for 60 hours per week, the
  Directors either work for about $1.00 per hour year-
  round or for two months at a reasonable salary and for
  10 months free.

* Volunteers from the community work at the Center on a
  regular basis; 4 hours of labor earns membership in the
  Center and 20 hours earn a T-shirt.

* Community groups such as Boy Scouts or 4-H occasionally
  work on curside collection routes.

Table 7. Categorical expenses as percentage of total
expenditures for Community Recycling Center,
1978-1981.

	1978		1979		1980		1981	
	$	%	$	%	$	%	$	%
Insurance	740	2.0	1,048	1.9	3,180	2.0	8,672	4.3
Telephone	54	0.1	445	0.8	1,425	0.9	1,959	1.0
Payment for recyclables	13	-	25	-	24,740	15.5	43,341	21.4
Publicity and promotion	106	0.3	1,377	2.4	2,497	1.6	2,876	1.4
Supplies	739	2.0	1,507	2.7	3,646	2.3	7,082	3.5
Building and equipment maintenance	124	0.3	1,043	1.9	2,172	1.4	1,677	0.8
Vehicle maintenance	325	0.9	2,876	5.1	7,372	4.7	3,366	1.7
Hauling	910	2.4	107	0.2	-	-	9,017	4.5
Gas and oil	73	0.2	1,084	1.9	6,861	4.3	7,258	3.6
Rent	490	1.3	2,583[a]	4.6	3,724	2.3	7,293	3.6
Administration	129	0.3	1,136	2.0	3,177	2.0	4,558	2.3
Landfill	9	-	386	0.7	730	0.5	1,014	0.5
Miscellaneous	184	0.5	411	0.7	3,676	2.3	2,293	1.1
CETA -- job training	33,995	89.7	35,614	63.3	83,238	52.5	83,989	41.5
Safety[b]	-	-	776	1.4	1,363	0.9	846	0.4
Grants excluding CETA	-	-	5,850	10.4	8,030	5.1	6,230	3.1
Petty cash	-	-	-	-	960	0.6	1,050	0.5
Salary	-	-	-	-	1,860	1.2	8,574	4.2
Curbside 6100PS	-	-	-	-	570	0.4	1,075	0.5
Interest	-	-	-	-	188	-	-	-
Total	37,891	100	56,268	100	158,508	100	202,350	100

---

[a] Includes truck payment

[b] Includes revenue sharing from local governments, ACTION funds
and National Center for Appropriate Technology grant.

* Volunteers from Students for Environmental Concerns
  and service fraternities at the University of Illinois
  regularly work at the Center.

* U. of I. professors have assigned CRC projects as class
  projects. Previous projects have involved civil engineering and advertising classes; current projects involve
  accounting and marketing classes.

* Persons on probation and other offenders perform
  service work at the Center.

* Two U. of I. graduate students in mechanical and industrial engineering have completed theses on projects
  related to the Center's operation.

* Countless other volunteers assist with educational and
  public relations programs, provide financial support,
  or donate time on various committees.

All these items must be taken into account to ascertain the
amount of work it actually requires to run the Center.

Even with subsidies, the Center only has managed to scrape by.
Now, with harsh CETA cutbacks, the outlook is more bleak. Steve
Apotheker, Director of the Center, recently remarked that, financially
speaking, the Center is "treading the fine line that runs next to the
abyss." The Center's Board of Directors is now reviewing and implemen
ting cost-saving measures. Despite the rocky times, Center staff are
confident the program will continue. The potential for major long-
term funding from the City is greater than ever before, and if this
becomes a reality, a major expansion of program operations can be
expected.

Are the Community Recycling Center's contributions to economic
development significant? Again, as with the Resource Center, the
answer is yes. Over the past four years more than 110 low-income
people have had job opportunities at CRC and nearly two-thirds of
their experiences have been positive. Significant amounts of money
are recirculated through the community each year via the aluminum
buy-back program. Troubled youth are provided opportunities for
service work. Community groups have opportunities to earn funds for
their projects. Plans are being made for curbside service in low-
income areas. These accomplishments are significant for a program
with such an inauspicious beginning.

For additional information, write the Community Recycling Center,
720 Market Street, Champaign IL 61820.

Options Recycling Team

Options, Inc. is one of 22 experimental companies that were started in 1975 to develop subsidized work programs as alternatives to the welfare system. The goals of Options are to launch enterprises that both create jobs for the poor and unskilled and earn revenues by providing goods and services to industry, government, and the community. Initial plans called for Options to become self-sufficient within five years while moving large numbers of chronically unemployed (ex-offenders, ex-addicts, drop-outs, and long-term welfare recipients) into the ranks of the gainfully employed. Despite lavish funding at its outset by government and foundations, Options has had only moderate success, and it has not reached its goal of financial independence.

The Options Recycling Team opened in April, 1981 as Option's newest venture. Considering Option's goals, recycling seemed an ideal activity. Jobs would be created and revenues would be generated. The benefits related to the conservation of energy and natural resources would be a bonus. It seemed an ideal business for an organization interested in community development to pursue.

The recycling program was developed as a labor intensive enterprise. The program manager, strongly influenced by Gandhi and E.F. Schumacher, sought to establish a work environment that emphasized production by the masses rather than mass production, with jobs for people rather than machines. Recycling was promoted as "good work" activities from which the workers could derive a true sense of dignity, self-worth, and accomplishment. Special effort was made to challenge and channel the talents and energies of the individual workers in directions that would result in both personal and project growth.

The Options Recycling Team, initially aided by good luck and generous assistance from Ken Dunn of the Resource Center, grew rapidly. From in-house recovery of wastes from other Options enterprises and mixed metals processing, the Recycling Team opened a buy-back program in July. Volume increased from 10 to more than 30 tons per month (Table 8). A high grade paper recovery program was added in September. Volume averaged 32 tons per month between July and November. Aluminum, bimetal cans, and high grade paper comprised the bulk of the materials processed. Monthly earnings from the sale of materials increased to nearly $6,700 per month.

Then problems began. Cutbacks in the CETA program hit Options hard, placing additional pressure on the Recycling Team to become financially self-sufficient. With the onset of winter, problems with the building that housed Options became apparent, and working conditions deteriorated.

Table 8. Income and expense summary of Options Recycling
Team, Inc. (April to December, 1981)

	April	May	June	July	August
Revenues and Subsidy					
Income	1,338	1,910	2,929	4,129	6,616
CETA Subsidy	2,453	2,973	3,447	4,105	3,597
Options funds	1,153	2,013	2,404	4,028	6,493
Total	4,944	6,896	8,780	12,262	16,706
Expenses					
Subsidies and wages	4,227	6,473	7,846	10,186	9,874
Miscellaneous, including supplies, equipment	717	423	392	158	615
Bimetal purchases	-	-	476	503	505
Publicity	-	-	66	-	-
Buy-Back	-	-	-	1,248	3,431
Overhead	-	-	-	-	1,481
Rent	-	-	-	167	-
Hauling	-	-	-	-	800
Total	4,944	6,896	8,780	12,262	16,706
Income as percentage of expenses	27%	28%	33%	34%	40%
CETA subsidy as percentage of expenses	50%	43%	39%	34%	22%
Options funds as percentage of expenses	23%	29%	28%	32%	38%

Table 8. Income and expense summary of Options Recycling Team, Inc. (April to December, 1981) (Continued)

	September	October	November	December	Total
Revenues and Subsidy					
Income	4,115	4,295	5,602	3,311	34,245
CETA subsidy	1,526	2,348	6,749	7,369	34,566
Options funds	7,834	6,498	6,066	6,038	42,527
Total	13,475	13,141	18,417	16,717	111,338
Expenses					
Subsidies and wages	8,286	7,565	12,437	11,121	78,015
Miscellaneous, including supplies, equipment	184	698	257	286	3,730
Bimetal purchases	252	81	73	92	1,982
Publicity	-	-	-	-	66
Buy-Back	3,210	3,362	3,384	3,262	17,897
Overhead	1,243	1,135	1,866	1,668	7,393
Rent	-	-	-	48	215
Hauling	300	300	400	240	2,040
Total	13,475	13,141	18,417	16,717	111,338
Income as percentage of expenses	31%	33%	30%	20%	31%
CETA subsidy as percentage of expenses	11%	18%	37%	44%	31%
Options funds as percentage of expenses	58%	49%	33%	36%	38%

143

The area used by the Recycling Team was without heat, was poorly lit (the area received no natural lighting), and after pipes froze and burst, was without toilet facilities. Because of these conditions, business hours were reduced and the buy-back program was closed intermittently. Worker productivity dropped. The volume of material brought to the Recycling Team also dropped, and revenues decreased. In early February of 1982, there was a major fire on the third and fourth floors at Options. The fire knocked out all electrical power and the freight elevators became inoperable. Shipping and receiving of materials became virtually impossible, and the Recycling Team shut down its operations. Its doors never reopened and the Recycling Team was disbanded that same month.

What went wrong? While there are a number of explanations, key factors in the decision to discontinue recycling appear to be related to financial and institutional considerations. Despite considerable progress, the Recycling Team did not become financially independent in its first eight months. Although a firm timetable for achieving financial independence never was established, cut backs in Federal CETA funds made self-sufficiency more important and hastened the Recycling Team's demise.

A review of its income and expense summary reveals that income from the sale of materials averaged just 31% of total expenditures (Table 9) and never accounted for more than 40% of expenditures during any month. CETA subsidies accounted for 31% of total expenditures. Revenues from the sales of materials dropped 41% between November and December, which was the worst month for Options in terms of self-sufficiency. Between September and December, Options contributed 44% of the total revenues needed to cover expenses for the Recycling Team. Apparently, because costs to Options for maintaining the Recycling Team were too high and the outlook for improvement appeared bleak, Options administrators made the decision to terminate the program.

The decision to terminate the recycling program may have been hastened because of the institutional parameters that govern Options. Options goals are to train unskilled, low-income people and to generate enough revenues to stay in business without subsidies. Recycling is tenable in the Options organization only as long as it meets these goals. There is no institutional commitment to recycling as such.

Despite the fact that it closed, it can be argued that the Recycling Team made a significant contribution to economic development in the neighborhood. At its largest, the Recycling Team included eighteen people. Gretchen Brewer, Team Manager, reported a "phenominal improvement" in the work attitudes and habits of most Team members

Several people previously unable to hold steady jobs, were successful in staying on the job and improving their performance to the
point where they were responsible and could be counted on to complete
assigned tasks. Most of the workers learned enough skills to operate
or manage a buy-back program themselves. The Team members' understanding of the problems of waste and garbage management also increased

The Recycling Team also helped neighborhood residents earn
needed cash. A large amount of waste materials were diverted from
the landfill. And perhaps most important, the program set the stage
for other recycling programs to be implemented in the area. Adults
and children still come to Options seeking to sell their recyclables.
This indicates that if a market were available, residents would respond
Former Team members now are exploring alternative ways to begin a new
program. Building from the experience gained while with Options, it
would not be surprising if they succeed.

Table 9. Sources of revenues and volume of recyclables for Options Recycling Team, Inc. (first nine months of operation)

Material	APRIL lbs.	%	$	%	MAY lbs.	%	$	%
Aluminum	990	4.8	347	25.9	2,088	7.2	721	37.7
Bimetal	13,306	64.3	844	63.1	13,660	47.0	884	46.3
Brass/Copper	-	-	-	-	-	-	-	-
Corrugated	5,000	24.2	129	9.6	9,505	33.0	205	10.7
Glass	300	1.4	5	0.4	408	1.4	6	0.3
Newspaper	800	3.9	-	-	800	2.8	12	0.6
Office Paper	-	-	-	-	250	0.9	250	13.1
Scrap Metal/Steel	300	1.4	13	1.0	350	1.2	11	0.6
Miscellaneous (a)	-	-	-	-	-	-	-	-
Total	20,696	100.0	1,338	100.0	29,061	100.0	1,910	100.0

Material	JUNE lbs.	%	$	%	JULY lbs.	%	$	%
Aluminum	2,182	4.3	764	26.1	2,400	14.4	2,400	58.1
Bimetal	33,099	64.8	1,882	64.3	24,550	52.0	1,582	38.3
Brass/Copper	-	-	-	-	-	-	-	-
Corrugated	12,864	25.2	180	6.1	9,085	19.2	134	3.2
Glass	828	1.6	10	0.3	2,953	6.3	6	0.1
Newspaper	800	1.6	-	-	3,142	6.7	31	0.8
Office Paper	-	-	-	-	-	-	-	-
Scrap Metal/Steel	1,274	2.5	41	1.4	690	1.5	13	0.3
Miscellaneous (a)	-	-	-	-	-	-	-	-
Total	51,047	100.0	2,929	100.0	47,220	100.0	4,130	100.0

AUGUST / SEPTEMBER

Material		AUGUST				SEPTEMBER	
	lbs.	%	$	%	lbs.	$	%
						%	
Aluminum	12,018	14.3	3,921	58.9	9,292	12.8	2,984	72.5
Bimetal	28,935	34.3	1,865	28.0	10,957	15.1	706	17.2
Brass/Copper	–	–	–	–	–	–	–	–
Corrugated	18,050	2.4	149	2.2	7,830	10.8	89	2.2
Glass	11,832	14.0	177	2.7	8,912	12.2	84	2.0
Newspaper	11,750	13.9	118	1.8	5,145	7.1	51	1.2
Office Paper	–	–	–	–	30,000	41.2	136	3.3
Scrap Metal/Steel	3,732	4.4	46	0.7	633	0.9	14	0.3
Miscellaneous (a)	–	–	340	5.1	–	–	51	1.2
Total	84,317	100.0	6,656	100.0	72,769	100.0	4,115	100.0

OCTOBER / NOVEMBER

Material		OCTOBER				NOVEMBER	
	lbs.	%	$	%	lbs.	%	$	%
Aluminum	9,499	15.1	3,027	70.5	10,431	14.9	3,243	62.0
Bimetal	–	–	–	–	11,250	16.1	500	9.6
Brass/Copper	290	0.5	290	6.8	300	0.4	300	5.7
Corrugated	5,040	8.0	67	1.6	4,000	5.7	35	0.7
Glass	9,382	15.0	138	3.2	8,659	12.4	130	2.5
Newspaper	1,700	2.7	17	0.4	7,850	11.2	79	1.5
Office Paper	33,000	52.6	825	19.2	22,100	31.6	983	18.8
Scrap Metal/Steel	3,373	5.4	41	1.0	5,050	7.2	38	0.7
Miscellaneous (a)	–	–	47	1.1	–	–	70	1.3
Total	62,751	100.0	4,295	100.0	69,939	100.0	5,228	100.0

(a) Revenues from refillable bottles. radiators. and a truck.

Table 9. Sources of revenues and volume of recyclables for Options Recycling Team, Inc. (first nine months of operation) (Continued)

Material	DECEMBER				TOTAL			
	lbs.	%	$	%	lbs.	%	$	%
Aluminum	8,468	19.3	2,650	80.0	61,768	16.0	19,697	57.5
Bimetal	-	-	-	-	135,757	35.2	8,263	24.1
Brass/Copper	-	-	-	-	590	0.2	590	1.7
Corrugated	390	0.9	2	-	71,764	18.6	990	2.9
Glass	5,214	11.9	78	2.4	48,488	12.6	634	1.9
Newspaper	1,700	3.9	17	0.5	33,687	8.7	325	0.9
Office Paper	26,000	59.3	461	13.9	85,811	22.2	2,425	7.1
Scrap Metal/Steel	1,243	2.8	10	0.3	15,412	4.0	227	0.7
Miscellaneous (a)	-	-	94	2.8	-	-	602	1.8
Total	43,839	100.0	3,311	100.0	385,813	100.0	34,245	100.0
					193.9 tons			

(a) Revenues from refillable bottles, radiators, and a truck.

Comparison of Existing Programs

Volume statistics and sources of revenues, categorical expenditures, and income and expense summaries for the Resource Center, the Community Recycling Center, and the Options Recycling Team are presented in Tables 10, 11, and 12, respectively. Highlights of each program are presented in Table 13.

These data indicate that the Resource Center is the most cost-efficient operation. Spending just $104,000 to recycle 3,400 tons of material, the average cost per ton of material recycled by the Resource Center was $41. Comparable figures for the Community Recycling Center and Options Recycling Team were $173 per ton and $574 per ton, respectively. The main reason for these differences are the amount of handling and hauling done by each operation. This method of comparison is extremely crude because:

* It does not adjust for expenses incurred by CRC or Options Recycling Team because of job training goals or for other purposes not considered recycling, per se (i.e., education, research).

* It does not adjust for differences in the types of wastes handled.

* It does not adjust for locational differences.

* It does not reflect contributions or benefits from volunteers.

Nevertheless, it is a revealing comparison that has a number of implications for new programs. Additional study, such as the analysis of the efficiency with which each item is handled (similar to CRC's analysis of its aluminum program) would be necessary to refine the comparison further.

The preceding comparison also gives an indication of the actual potential for recycling to contribute to economic development in a low-income neighborhood. The Resource Center, for example, employs eight people and annually circulates approximately $100,000 through the neighborhoods of Hyde Park and Woodlawn. The Resource Center primarily serves the 67,251 People who reside in Hyde Park-Woodlawn. Although these numbers are not large, they are significant.

The numbers are especially significant in the eyes of those who are employed by the Center or those who rely on sales of recyclables for needed cash. The potential for additional programs is great, and with hard work and dedication, new programs could be developed. The population of Chicago is approximately 3 million. If one center were developed for each 67,000 people, there would be 45 Resource Centers in the City, employing 360 people. About $4,500,000 would be added to Chicago's economy. This is significant. And without action by concerned individuals, it is an opportunity that is literally going to waste.

Table 10. Materials recycled and sources of revenues by percent for the Resource Center, Community Recycling Center, and Options, Inc.

| | RESOURCE CENTER 1980-81 | | COMMUNITY RECYCLING CENTER 1981 | | OPTIONS, INC. 1981 | |
	Volume 3,400 tons	Revenues $103,976	Volume 1,167.4 tons	Revenues[a] $100,613	Volume 193.9 tons	Revenues[b] $34,245
	%	%	%	%	%	%
Glass	13.7	6.9	31.0	12.8	12.6	1.9
Newspaper	30.5	30.5	38.9	6.2	8.7	0.9
Cardboard	38.2	23.0	10.0	2.5	18.6	2.9
White Paper	4.6	0.4	–	–	–	–
High Grade/Office	–	–	2.8	1.1	22.2	7.1
Tin/Steel	3.1	4.6	3.4	2.6	–	–
Bimetal	–	–	2.6	5.6	35.2	24.1
Aluminum	6.1	32.1	7.2	54.9	16.0	57.5
Scrap	0.8	–	1.0	–	4.0	0.7
Mixed Paper	–	–	3.4	–	–	–
Oil (gallons)	–	–	25,242[d]	6.3	–	–
Refillables	–	–	–	0.2	–	–
Interest	–	–	–	0.1	–	–
Miscellaneous	–	2.5[c]	–	7.6	–	1.8[e]

a Does not include subsidy. 1981 subsidy totalled $92,714.

b Does not include subsidy. 1981 subsidy totalled $77,093.

c Includes revenues from scrap.

d Does not include 3,000 gallons collected but not sold.

e Includes revenues from refillables, radiators.

151

Table 11. Categorical expenditures by percent for Resource Center, Community Recycling Center, and Options, Inc.

Category	RESOURCE CENTER 1980-81 Total Expenditures $104,150 %	COMUNITY RECYCLING CENTER 1981 Total Expenditures $202,356 %	OPTIONS, INC. 1981 Total Expenditures $111,338 %
Insurance	–	4.3	–
Telephone	0.5	1.0	–
Payment for Recyclables	35.3	21.4	17.9
Publicity and Promotion	–	1.4	c
Supplies	–	3.5	–
Building & Equipment Maintenance & Equipment Losses	–	0.8	–
Vehicle Repair & Maintenance	4.6	1.7	–
Hauling, Gas & Oil	1.7	8.1	1.8
Rent/Property Taxes	2.1	3.6	0.2
Administration & Legal Fees (General Overhead)	1.2	2.3	6.6
Landfill	–	0.5	–
Safety	–	0.4	–
Salary	50.4	4.2	70.0[d]
CETA/Job Training	–	41.5	e
Grants, Excluding CETA	–	3.1	–
Curbside Groups	–	0.5	–
Petty Cash	–	0.5	–
Miscellaneous, including interest	0.5	1.2	3.4[b]
Depreciation	3.7	–	–

(a) Also includes building and equipment repair and maintenance.
(b) Also includes general supplies and equipment.
(c) Less than 0.1%.
(d) Includes $34,566 from CETA. Therefore, CETA related expenditures were 31% of total expenditures.
(e) Included in salary.

Table 12. Income and expense summaries for Community Recycling Center (1978–1981), Resource Center (1980–81), and Options Recycling Team (1981)

	Revenues $	Expenditures $	Revenues as % of Expenditures %	Loss from Operations Excluding Subsidy $	Subsidy $	Subsidy % of Expenditures %	Net Increase from Operation $	Assets $	Liabilities $	Change in Equity $
Community Recycling Center										
1978	5,473	38,891	14	32,418	33,995	87	1,653	2,075	0	2,075
1979	15,978	56,268	28	40,290	42,764	76	2,491	8,751	1,778	4,897
1980	58,534	158,508	37	99,975	91,268	58	(8,706)	14,094	12,025	2,069
1981	100,613	202,356	50	101,743	92,714	46	NA	NA	NA	NA
Resource Center[b]										
1980-81	103,976	104,150	99.8	174	-	-	NA	47,266	18,805[a]	NA
Options Recycling Team[c]										
1981	34,245	111,338	31	77,093[d]	77,093	69	NA	NA	NA	NA

(a) Includes $17,262 in accrued salary.
(b) Data is for most recent fiscal year.
(c) Data is for first nine months of operation (April-December).
(d) Subsidy includes $34,566 from CETA and $42,527 in Options funds.

NA = Not Available.

153

Table 13. 1981 Program highlights for the Resource Center, Community Recycling Center, and Options Recycling Team

RESOURCE CENTER	COMMUNITY RECYCLING CENTER	OPTIONS RECYCLING TEAM
* Financially self-sufficient	* 46% of expenditures subsidized	* 69% of expenditures subsidized
* Spent $104,000 to recycle 3,400 tons; average cost of $41/ton	* Spent $202,000 to recycle 1,167 tons; average cost of $173/ton	* Spent $111,338 to recycle 194 tons; average cost of $574/ton
* Most expenditures for salary (50%) and payment for recyclables (35%)	* Most expenditures for salary (48%) and payment for recyclables (21%)	* Most expenditures for salary (70%) and payment for recyclables (18%)
* Aluminum source of most earned revenues (32%)	* Aluminum source of most earned revenues (55%)	* Aluminum source of most earned revenues (58%)
* Cardboard, greatest volume by weight	* Newsprint greatest volume by weight	* Bimetal greatest volume by weight
* Buy-back operation accounts for 70% of recyclables handles	* Drop-off sites account for most recyclables, except for aluminum	* Relationship with other waste handlers (bimetal and high grade) accounted for greatest portion of volume

154

* Little processing of materials, handling minimized; short distance to markets

* Organizational commitment to recycling; relies heavily on dedication and extra work by manager

* All glass handled and crushed; aluminum flattened; long distance to markets

* Organizational commitment to recycling; Director and Assistant Director both severely underpaid; volunteers assist with all aspects of operation

* Hand sorting of bimetal cans and of high-grade paper; short distance to markets

* No organizational commitment to recycling, per se; no volunteer assistance

Recommendations

Based on the preceding analysis of recycling operations several general recommendations for new programs are made. These should be viewed as general guidelines only; nothing substitutes for actual experience. If, when trying to initiate a new program, you find that something works, by all means do it. Don't worry about written guidelines. Remember that recycling is hard work, but also remember too that it does work.

1. Visit and work at other recycling programs.

    The best way to learn about recycling is to visit centers and to work at them. Talking with practitioners is the best way to obtain current information. Manuals such as this become dated and present only general guidelines that may change with time. Most people that run recycling programs are extremely willing to help and share their experience. Remember, however, that recycling managers probably are overworked and burdened by problems with their own programs. An offer to volunteer will be looked at favorably. Take a trip to a market with someone; time spent in the cab of a truck is a good way to make double use of your time.

2. Begin a buy-back program.

    In low-income areas, buy-back programs are most effective because they give local residents a direct, economic incentive to recycle. Buy-back programs reduce collection costs because recyclers bring materials to the center. Because the recyclables are being purchased, they can be rejected if they have not been prepared properly. Recyclables can be placed directly into the containers in which they will be shipped, thus reducing handling and processing time.

3. Concentrate initially on aluminum recycling.

    As demonstrated, aluminum currently is the most valuable recyclable and offers the greatest potential for cost effective operation. Although competition for cans is extremely fierce, nonprofit, community-based programs can compete. It is important to establish prices competitive with those of operations already in existence. Aluminum recyclers will travel significant distances for better prices and are not particularly concerned about whether they sell to a neighborhood group or to a private business. A margin of 5¢ between the price paid for the aluminum and the price for which the aluminum is sold appears to be a minimum breakeven point for labor-intensive programs. Revenues from aluminum sales help pay for the recycling of other less valuable recyclables.

4. Initially, for all materials, try to arrange with markets to provide containers or vehicles for storage and hauling.

   See Markets and Equipment sections of this manual. Complete negotiations with markets prior to opening operation. Know what price markets will pay and set purchase prices accordingly. Resource Center and Options Recycling Team prices are examples for buy-back pricing. If markets provide containers, they will offer a lower price. This is acceptable because it minimizes start-up costs for capital items. Typical vehicles for hauling are:

> * Aluminum - enclosed semi-trailer
> * Newsprint - enclosed semi-trailer
> * Glass - 20 cubic yard roll-off container
> * Steel and bimetal cans - 20 cubic yard roll -off container
> * Cardboard - enclosed semi-trailer

   Bimetal processors are beginning to sponsor buy-back programs similar to aluminum collections sponsored by can companies. It will be most difficult to locate containers for glass and steel cans because glass manufacturers and steel processors usually do not spot containers. In Chicago, coordinate with the Resource Center. Hauling arrangements may be possible with some type of barter arrangement.

5. Budget about half of projected expenses for salary, wages, and related items.

   The preceding review of operating costs for the three programs indicates that salary-related costs ranged from 48% to 70% of total expenses. Salary-related costs were highest for the Options Recycling Team, the newest program and the one that relied least on volunteer labor. These figures are useful for initial budgeting. As a general guideline, expect total expenses to double salaries and wages.

For example, if a new program initially will be managed
by one person who wants to earn $600 per month, total
expenses ranging from $860 to $1200 should be budgeted.
In other words, to earn $600 per month by recycling, a
person must sell at least $1200 worth of recyclables.
Remember that because this generalization is drawn
from programs that rely heavily on volunteer labor and
extraordinary efforts by staff, salary-related expenses
may comprise a greater percentage of total expenses.

6. Minimize handling.

     Wherever possible, reduce intermediate processing and
handling. If possible, set up operation so that once mat
erial is purchased, it is place directly into hauling
vehicle/container. Collection is inherently less efficient for small, labor-intensive programs because it
involves the extra step of loading and unloading the
collection vehicles and because it eliminates the quality control possible with a buy-back program.

7. Know the product.

     The product that you will sell is scrap: old, used
cans, bottles, and paper. Learn what factors influence
prices for these materials and why prices change. Learn
to estimate scrap volumes and values.

* Aluminum currently sells for slightly over 30¢ per pound
  (1982). Thirty cents per pound equals $600 per ton.
  Therefore, to earn $1200 (see recommendation #4), 2 tons
  of aluminum cans are needed. Two tons of loose cans would
  fill a 40 foot semi-trailer approximately half-full,
  assuming that there were both crushed and uncrushed cans.
  A semi-trailer will held between 7,000 and 10,000 pounds
  of cans when full depending on the mix of crushed and
  uncrushed cans. A trailer will hold 16,000 pounds of
  crushed cans.

* Newsprint currently sells for anywhere from $10 to $40
  per ton (1982) depending on its quality and the market.
  A 40 foot semi-trailer holds between 18 and 22 tons
  of loose newsprint depending on how high it is stacked.

* Glass now sells for between $35 and $50 per ton (1982),
  depending on volume and market. Some markets offer
  premiums for glass recycled via buy-back programs.
  About 10 tons of slightly crushed glass will fit in
  a 20 cubic yard roll-off container (the glass is broken
  only as it enters the container; no effort is made to
  crush the bottles manually).

8. Know about waste management in the service area.

Before beginning, study the waste management system
in your area. Know how much waste is generated and where
it is going. Identify other recycling programs. Knowing
how much waste is in the area will enable you to gauge
the effectiveness of the program; i.e., determine what
percentage is being recycled.

In Chicago, the Bureau of Engineering of the Department of Public Works has estimated waste generation by
Ward and the average or typical waste stream composition
in the City. The Bureau also has "investigated the
feasibility" of source separation. These data and the
findings are presented in the report: *Chicago Resource
Recovery Study, Phase I*, prepared in June 1981 by Envir-
odyne Engineers, Inc. Review of this document will provide a good summary of the waste management system in
Chicago.

Be aware that the study has limitations. For example
the waste stream analysis is an average for the entire
City. The fact is that waste generation differs throughout the City. Both the amounts of waste and the types
of waste differ depending on the income level and the
ethnic make-up of the area. Although no detailed waste
stream studies are available for Chicago, recent studies
of five neighborhoods in Milwaukee (Rathju and Thompson,
The Milwaukee Garbage Project, 1981) reveal that:

*   Sample households in the two low-income and in one
    middle-income area discarded more refuse overall
    than households in the other two areas (moderately-
    low-income and middle-income).

*   Sample households in the two low-income areas dis-
    carded more packaging by weight than sample house-
    holds in the other areas.

*   The discarding of aluminum seems to increase as
    income decreases.

Final Words

Now, begin. Despite relatively poor market con
ditions caused by the recessionary economy, there is
a considerable amount of activity, especially in the
Chicago metropolitan area. The Resource Center, in
cooperation with the former program manager of the
Options Recycling Team, is planning small recycling
cooperatives that would begin buy-back programs in
vacant lots or buildings throughout Chicago. Sierra
Club members are trying to find a permanent location
for a center. The Department of Energy and Natural
Resources and the North Shore Ecology Center have
cooperatively published this manual. The Illinois
Association of Recycling Centers is growing stronger
and is able to lend some assistance to new programs.
Markets for bimetal cans are expanding. All in all,
it is a good time to begin. Good luck.

Appendix I: Funding Resources

You have a vision of how your community can be a better place in which to live, and you plan to operate a recycling center to make it happen. You have an organization to implement your plans, and it has members willing to do the work. What else do you need?

MONEY! As an active member of an ambitious organization, you know it takes money to run your program. Once your project is initiated and running, you will have revenues from the sale of the recyclables you collect to work with, but until you can call your project a success, where will you find the dollars you need?

Fundraising is an art in itself, but you do not have to be an expert to get what you need to start up a recycling project. The first step is to know what you need and how much. Then go to those who have it and ask Don't be shy! Afterall, you're not asking for yourself; you are asking for the support of a project to improve your community for all its residents and business people.

So, by all means, begin your fundraising efforts right in your own community. Those chamber of commerce members, business leaders, civic organizations, public officials, and activists you contacted early in your planning stages all have resources they might make available to you for a good cause.

Ask them for dollars and sense . . . yes, _sense_! They might not give you the dollars you ask for, but may be very happy to donate the item or service you needed the money for in the first place -- or they might have other suggestions for ways of raising the money you need. Make sense now?

There are numerous other ways to raise money for your project. Through membership drives, raffles, ad books, bake sales, bingo games, door-to-door solicitations, and a variety of other local fundraising events, many local groups have been able to raise all or most of their operating budgets.

In determining just what fundraising projects might be most profitable for your group, the following book is highly recommended. _The Grass Roots Fundraising Book_ by Joan Flanagan for the Youth Project (Chicago: The Swallow Press, Inc., 1977, $4.75). If you cannot find this book in your local library or bookstore, order it from "The Youth Project" 1000 Wisconsin Ave., N.W., Washington D.C. 20007.

Other Fundraising Resources

THE DONORS FORUM
208 S. LaSalle Street
Chicago IL 60604
(312) 726-4877

If you seek funds from foundations or corporations, information about your organization should be in the Donors' Forum organizational file. This file is kept in the Donors' Forum Library and is used by foundations and corporations in their grantmaking to find information about area organizations. The Donors' Forum library also contains extensive materials about private and public funding sources.

The Donors' Forum also publishes *Can Do II, A Technical Assistance Guide* by Paul A. Lehman and Patricia Wyzbinski, 1980. Offers detailed information about providers of technical assistance (TA) in the Chicago metropolitan area, as well as thoughtful essays about the TA field and helpful hints for consumers on locating and making the most of TA.

Government Programs

There may be several grant programs available through city, state, and federal offices of solid waste management and environmental quality Begin with your local municipality and also write the following agencies for information on specific grant opportunities in your area.

ILLINOIS ENVIRONMENTAL
 PROTECTION AGENCY
2200 Churchill Road
Springfield, IL 62706

ILLINOIS DEPARTMENT OF
 ENERGY & NATURAL RESOURCES
325 W. Adams
Springfield, IL 62706

ILLINOIS DEPARTMENT OF
 COMMERCE & COMMUNITY AFFAIRS
222 S. College
Springfield, IL 62706

U.S. ENVIRONMENTAL PROTECTION
 AGENCY, REGION V OFFICE
230 S. Dearborn
Chicago, IL 60604

U.S. DEPARTMENT OF HEALTH
 & HUMAN SERVICES
300 S. Wacker Drive
Chicago, IL 60606

Appendix II:

Publicity Samples of Illinois Recycling Programs

RECYCLING
It makes $ense for America

**It conserves your tax dollars
saves space in our limited landfills
conserves natural resources**

Today America is faced with critical shortages of energy and natural resources. The resources once thought to be unlimited are now being depleted; worse yet, some are irreplaceable.

Recycling represents our best solution towards solving many of our nation's energy problems, but the success of this depends on you! Wise use of our resources and recycling of most of our waste products will not only conserve energy, they will preserve our limited resources.

The Niles West High School Recycling Center asks that each and every citizen participate in the Village's recycling program. Glass bottles and jars, cans, and newspapers are accepted at the recycling center located at 7929 Austin, behind the Niles West High School football stadium. The recycling center is open Wednesday thru Saturdays from 8:00 a.m. to 5:00 p.m.

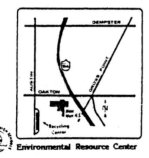

Environmental Resource Center

HOURS
WED. thru FRI
8a.m.- 5p.m.
SAT. 8a.m.- 5p.m.
Closed Sunday thru tuesday

470-0242

Recycling saves trees. This is 100 percent recycled paper

RECYCLE
Newspaper - Magazines - Catalogues

for information call

North Shore Ecology Center

Northbrook Village Hall parking lot 432-1440	Elm Place and the railroad tracks Highland Park 432-1440	1390 Willow Rd Winnetka 432-1440
Western Ave at the Water Tower Lake Forest 432-1440	Niles West High School 7929 Austin Ave Skokie 966-3800	Municipal parking lot Green Bay & Park Ave Glencoe 432-1440

61	Recycling		61	Recycling

Don't throw it away . . . RECYCLE IT!

Now courtesy of The News-Gazette you can recycle your unwanted goods by placing a want ad in The News-Gazette's Classified 61 Recycling section for FREE. If you have things you're not using that someone else may be able to use like clothing glass jars cardboard boxes etc — RECYCLE THEM! Phone or bring in your recycling ad to The News-Gazette. Your ad will appear for 3 days for FREE. All ads should be 15 words or less and MUST include the word FREE in reference to the items offered. So put your recycleables to use — place your ad today!

Classified 351-5288
The News-Gazette

RECYCLE

166

N.A.R.C.*

*(NAPERVILLE AREA RECYCLING CENTER)

THANK YOU FOR BRINGING YOUR RECYCLABLES TO THE N.A.R.C.
WITHOUT YOUR HELP WE CAN'T CONTINUE. THE MORE YOU
BRING FOR RECYCLING THE BETTER FOR US, FOR YOU, AND
FOR THE ENVIRONMENT. WOULD YOU LIKE TO HELP US? WE
ALWAYS NEED VOLUNTEERS. CAN YOU COME FOR THREE HOURS
ON A SATURDAY ONCE EVERY TWO MONTHS? FOR MORE INFOR-
MATION CALL   ANNE 420-7047   OR SALLY 420-2439.

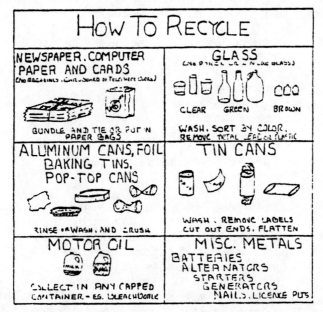

HOW TO RECYCLE

NEWSPAPER, COMPUTER PAPER AND CARDS
(NO MAGAZINES, CARDBOARD OR TELEPHONE BOOKS)

BUNDLE AND TIE OR PUT IN PAPER BAGS

GLASS
(NO PYREX OR WINDOW GLASS)

CLEAR   GREEN   BROWN

WASH, SORT BY COLOR, REMOVE METAL LEAD OR PLASTIC

ALUMINUM CANS, FOIL BAKING TINS, POP-TOP CANS

RINSE OR WASH, AND CRUSH

TIN CANS

WASH, REMOVE LABELS CUT OUT ENDS, FLATTEN

MOTOR OIL

COLLECT IN ANY CAPPED CONTAINER - E.G. BLEACH BOTTLE

MISC. METALS
BATTERIES
ALTERNATORS
STARTERS
GENERATORS
NAILS, LICENCE PLTS

HOURS: 9-3 SATURDAY   PLACE: JACKSON AT MILL

FLYER DONATED BY AMERICAN ASSOCIATION OF UNIVERSITY WOMEN
(TAPE INSIDE KITCHEN CABINET DOOR FOR FUTURE REFERENCE)

Hazel Crest
(Cave Memorial)
Recycle Center

Where   The recycle center is located at the north end of California St., next to Oak Hill Park.

When   The Recycle Center is open every Saturday from 10:00 a.m. to 4:00 p.m.

What   The Recycle Center will accept:
Paper, glass, aluminum, tin, and used motor oils
(Preparation details on other side)

Who   The Recycle Center is managed and staffed by volunteers from organizations and groups from Hazel Crest.

Why   The Recycle Center was established to conserve natural resources, maintain ecology, and enrich our village. All profits realized from the operation of the center will be distributed to the organizations or groups of indivuduals which staff the Center. Qualifying organizations or groups must submit a Letter of Intent to use the money received to support ecology, village beautification, village services, or youth activities.

**We need your help now
to make the Center a success·**

RECYCLING
RESOURCE RECLAMATION

You're probably doing it right now, without even realizing it. Passing clothing on from one child to the next is a kind of recycling. Another is refinishing an old piece of furniture rather than buying a new one. Recycling is reusing paper, cloth, plastic, and metal containers whenever possible instead of throwing them away.

Mc Henry County Defenders are promoting this practice of "resource reclamation" and everyone can help. The homemaker is the most important person in the family's efforts towards recycling. Once parents set the example, children become eager helpers.

Every family, school, and business can participate in recycling. Newspapers, corrugated board, glass containers, "tin" cans, all-aluminum cans, and oil, are collected in Cary, Crystal Lake, Harvard, Mc Henry, and Woodstock, on a regular basis. Local newspapers and WIVS radio carry information about these drives. Be sure to check the date, time, and place each month. Also make certain your recyclable materials are properly prepared before bringing them to the collection site. (See Defenders' "Recycling Fact Sheet" for instructions on what to save and how to prepare it.) This makes the work of the volunteers much easier.

The homemaker can practice recycling in many other ways. Take grocery bags back to the store for refilling. Plastic bags from bread, etc., can be reused for food storage. Carefully washed, they make an excellent stuffing for water and mildew-proof pillows. Try sponges, washable dishcloths, and rags instead of paper towels. How about cloth instead of disposable diapers? Saves money, too!

Children will enjoy art projects using cans, bottles, popsicle sticks, old greeting cards, "junk" mail, and other materials we often discard. How about composting yard and kitchen wastes? (See Defenders' "How to Make a Compost Pile".) A dedicated few are recycling bacon drippings and other animal fats by making their own soap. (Ask for a copy of our home-made toilet soap recipe.) These are everyday reclamations that snowball into real contributions towards saving our valuable and diminishing natural resources.

The Defenders' Recycling Committee is currently active in the monthly recycling drives in Crystal Lake and Mc Henry, and has provided technical knowledge for groups in several other communities to start their own recycling programs.

The committee has also studied the feasibility of setting up a recycling plant in the county, and is encouraging efforts by private operators to get into this field on a large scale. For the future, recycling is the only logical way to deal with our solid waste problem.

If your group, club, school, or organization is interested in learning more about resource reclamation, members of the Recycling Committee will present an informative program on this subject anywhere in Mc Henry County. Contact Sherry Anderson, 338-5539, for further details on this free service.

MC HENRY COUNTY DEFENDERS
dedicated to the protection of the land and natural resources of McHenry County

Box 603, Crystal Lake, Illinois 60014

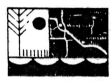

McHENRY COUNTY DEFENDERS

| Who Are We?

We were born in the spring of 1970 and since then have grown from a small nucleus of half-a-dozen dedicated persons to an ever-increasing membership of over 200. Our members live in many different areas of the county. Some are students. Some are senior citizens. We vary in occupation, economic situation and political persuasion. We are non-political and not-for-profit.

WHAT ARE WE "DEFENDING"?

The one thing we all have in common is a growing concern about the future of the natural environment of our county. As population pressures increase, we see growing abuse of our air, our soil, of plant and animal life and of our precious water supplies. We believe that the future is too important to leave to chance. We are working hard to ensure that this land which we enjoy will continue to serve the needs of our children and their children.

HOW DO WE WORK TO ACCOMPLISH OUR GOALS?

We inform ourselves:
1. By participating in study groups on recycling, pesticides, gravel pits, zoning, planning for land use, and conservation.
2. By attending informative meetings and seminars.
3. Through attendance as observers at meetings of the County Board, zoning boards, city councils.

We inform others:
1. With our bi-monthly newsletter.
2. By encouraging citizen participation in our community recycling drives, such as the one in Crystal Lake, now starting its 7th year.
3. By holding public meetings several times a year. Recent meetings have dealt with flooding problems in the county, nuclear hazards, solid waste disposal, energy conservation and solar energy, the county zoning ordinance, and organic gardening.
4. By presenting such major events as the Land Use Seminar, Fox River Symposium, the Conference on Growth, the Energy Fair, and Solar NOW.
5. By maintaining an active Speakers Bureau.
6. By working with schools and other organizations giving suggestions and help on their environmental projects.
7. By sponsoring an enthusiastic Junior Defenders group.
8. With our Green Banks planting program for erosion control.
9. With newspaper releases, radio announcements, free fact sheets, and displays on many environmental topics.

We inform our public officials:
1. By keeping in close touch with them via conferences, calls and letters.
2. By testifying at public hearings.
3. By encouraging their attendance at our educational meetings.

We are dedicated, ambitious, enthusiastic, knowledgeable ... and overworked!

WILL YOU JOIN US?

Phones: 455-0567
338-1865
385-8512

P.O. Box 603
Crystal Lake, Illinois 60014
300/5/77

This is
a forest.

Each year 350,000 tons of paper (equivalent to 5,950,000 trees) are consumed in the Chicago area for the production of newsprint. Newsprint is easily recycled. Unfortunately, most newspaper is manufactured from virgin material because not enough paper is recycled. Last year, we recycled about one-third of the amount we consumed, or 98,000 tons. We could do better, and you can help! Your recycling efforts prevent the unnecessary destruction of trees, consume less energy, and cause far less pollution than does the manufacturing of materials from virgin resources.

Recycling saves tax dollars. The more materials we recycle (and paper accounts for 49% of our wastes), the less we send to the landfill. Our landfills are filling up fast, and the farther our garbage is hauled, the more it will cost us, the taxpayers!

Recycling...it's good for our economy. It's better for our environment!

This is where to save it.

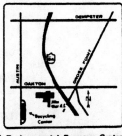

Environmental Resource Center
7929 Austin Avenue, Skokie.

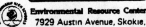

470-0242

Recycling saves trees This is 100 percent recycled paper

172

Conserve Energy !
RECYCLE

GLASS   CANS
NEWSPAPER

Solid Waste Reclamation Program
7929 Austin Avenue, Skokie, IL. 60076

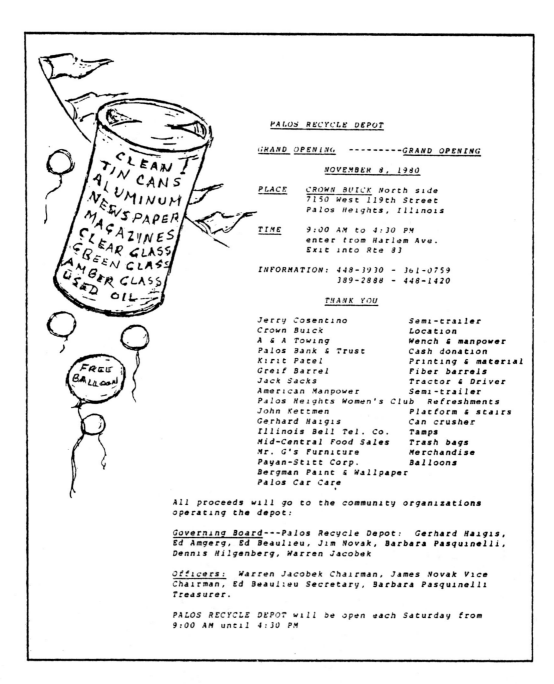

PALOS RECYCLE DEPOT

GRAND OPENING ---------GRAND OPENING

NOVEMBER 8, 1980

PLACE   CROWN BUICK North side
           7150 West 119th Street
           Palos Heights, Illinois

TIME   9:00 AM to 4:30 PM
           enter from Harlem Ave.
           Exit into Rte 83

INFORMATION: 448-3930 - 361-0759
             389-2888 - 448-1420

THANK YOU

Jerry Cosentino	Semi-trailer
Crown Buick	Location
A & A Towing	Wench & manpower
Palos Bank & Trust	Cash donation
Kirit Patel	Printing & material
Greif Barrel	Fiber barrels
Jack Sacks	Tractor & Driver
American Manpower	Semi-trailer
Palos Heights Women's Club	Refreshments
John Kettmen	Platform & stairs
Gerhard Haigis	Can crusher
Illinois Bell Tel. Co.	Tamps
Mid-Central Food Sales	Trash bags
Mr. G's Furniture	Merchandise
Payan-Stitt Corp.	Balloons
Bergman Paint & Wallpaper	
Palos Car Care	

All proceeds will go to the community organizations
operating the depot:

Governing Board---Palos Recycle Depot: Gerhard Haigis,
Ed Amgerg, Ed Beaulieu, Jim Novak, Barbara Pasquinelli,
Dennis Hilgenberg, Warren Jacobek

Officers: Warren Jacobek Chairman, James Novak Vice
Chairman, Ed Beaulieu Secretary, Barbara Pasquinelli
Treasurer.

PALOS RECYCLE DEPOT will be open each Saturday from
9:00 AM until 4:30 PM

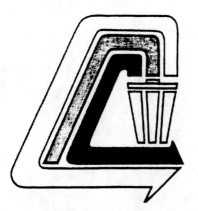

COMMUNITY RECYCLING CENTER
720 NORTH MARKET STREET
CHAMPAIGN, ILLINOIS 61820
217-351-4495

RECYCLE

The Community Recycling Center is a not for profit, tax exempt corporation whose main purposes are:

Recycling:

The Center recycles glass, cans, paper, cardboard, and used motor oil. People separate recyclable items at home and deposit them at the Center or one of the drop-off points throughout the community. The Center also collects recyclables from local businesses such as restaurants, bars, and elderly housing complexes which generate high volumes of waste. A buy-back program allows people to earn money for aluminum cans, foil, and scrap. These materials are all prepared for shipping and then sold to industries that make them into new products.

WITH YOUR HELP & SUPPORT

Education:

The Center provides speakers to interested groups to talk about recycling and solid waste problems. Staff members also give tours of the Center. In cooperation with Center staff, University students develop individual or class projects designed to improve or expand Center programs. The Center also publishes a monthly newsletter and has a slide-cassette show available for elementary students.

Job Training:

The Center cooperates with several community organizations to work with economically disadvantaged people and juvenile offenders to develop better job habits and new skills such as truck driving and forklift operation.

WHY RECYCLE?

After 1½ years of curbside collection, only 15% of the people offered the service participate. At least 30% participation must be achieved to continue the operation beyond 1981.

Approximately 40% of your "garbage" is recyclable. Recycling:

- Reduces energy consumption
- Saves landfill space
- Conserves scarce natural resources
- Reduces disposal costs
- Decreases pollution
- Creates jobs

CRC staff includes economically disadvantaged people, handicapped people, dropouts, and offenders. Recycling offers these groups meaningful community work while providing them with good work habits and job skills. Community groups can earn money by helping with curbside collection. Recycling is a solution that depends upon people instead of machines and money, but it does take your help. Please do your part for yourself and the community by recycling.

people working together

HOW YOU CAN HELP

RECYCLE: This is the most important way to help our efforts. If you already participate, encourage your friends and neighbors to begin. Also check the list of items to make sure you recycle everything presently possible.

DONATE: Although the Center plans to become self-sustaining through the sale of recyclables and donations, it will be several years before this is possible. Donations are used to offset operating expenses and purchase capital equipment that will help increase our efficiency. People who donate $20 or volunteer 4 hours of work become members of the Center. Members receive a monthly newsletter and can vote in annual elections for the Governing Council.

it's time for a new day recycle

VOLUNTEER: Saturdays and Sunday mornings are good times to help us collect, sort, and process materials. Committees on publicity, education, technical development, fundraising, and job training are in need of members. Committees do long range planning and help develop special projects. Groups can earn money by providing people to help with Saturday curbside collections.

REACT: Use your political and economic power to aid recycling efforts. Let governmental agencies and your elected representatives know you support recycling. Buy recycled products where possible and support the use of recycled materials in products. Subscribe to our newsletter to keep up-to-date on what is happening with recycling locally and nationally.

Appendix III: Additional Sources of Information

ALCOA RECYCLING COMPANY
2810 Alcoa Building
Pittsburgh, PA 15219

THE ALUMINUM ASSOCIATION
818 Connecticut Ave., N.W.
Washington, D.C. 20006

AMERICAN CAN COMPANY
American Lane
Greenwich, CT 06830

AMERICAN IRON & STEEL
  INSTITUTE
1000-16th Street, N.W.
Washington, D.C. 20036

AMERICAN PAPER INSTITUTE
Paper Stock Conservation Committee
260 Madison Avenue
New York, N.Y. 10016

AMERICAN PUBLIC WORKS
  ASSOCIATION
1313 East 60th Street
Chicago, IL 60637

NATIONAL ASSOCIATION OF COUNTIES
1735 New York Avenue, N.W.
Washington, D.C. 20006

NATIONAL ASSOCIATION OF RECYCLING
  INDUSTRIES
330 Madison Avenue
New York, N.Y. 20017

NATIONAL CAN COMPANY
8101 W. Higgins Road
Chicago, IL 60631

NATIONAL CENTER FOR RESOURCE
  RECOVERY
1211 Connecticut Ave., N.W.
Washington, D.C. 20036

NATIONAL GOVERNORS ASSOCIATION
444 N. Capitol Street
Washington, D.C. 20001

NATIONAL RECYCLING COALITION
45 Rockefeller Plaza
Room 2350
New York, N.Y. 10111

CAN MANUFACTURERS INSTITUTE
1625 Massachusetts Ave., N.W.
Washington, D.C. 20036

THE CONTINENTAL GROUP, INC.
633 Third Avenue
New York, N.Y. 10017

GLASS PACKAGING INSTITUTE
1800 K Street, N.W.
Washington, D.C. 20006

INSTITUTE FOR SCRAP IRON
AND STEEL
1627 K Street, N.W.
Washington, D.C. 20006

INTERNATIONAL CITY MANAGE-
MENT ASSOCIATION
1140 Connecticut Ave., N.S.
Washington, D.C. 20009

KAISER ALUMINUM
Recycling Department
300 Lakeside Drive
Oakland, CA 94643

MANUFACTURING CHEMISTS
ASSOCIATION
1825 Connecticut Ave., N.W.
Washington, D.C. 20009

NATIONAL TECHNICAL INFORMATION
SERVICE
5285 Port Royal Road
Springfield, Virginia 22161

NATIONAL TIRE DEALERS AND
RETREADERS ASSOCIATION
1343 L Street, N.W.
Washington, D.C. 20005

PAPERBOARD PACKAGING COUNCIL
1800 K Street, N.W.
Washington, D.C. 20006

REYNOLDS METALS COMPANY
800/22-2525
Call Toll Free

U.S. DEPT. OF THE INTERIOR
Bureau of Mines
2401 E. Street, N.W.
Washington, D.C. 20241

U.S. ENVIRONMENTAL PROTECTION
AGENCY, SOLID WASTE MGMT. OFFICE
401 M Street, S.W.
Washington, D.C. 20460

Appendix IV: References

1 Oregon Department of Environmental Quality, Solid Waste Division, "Where Does Your Garbage Go?" Portland: April, 1980, p. 1.

2 IBID, p. 1.

3 Hoy, Suellen M. and Michael C. Robinson. Recovering the Past: A Handbook of Community Recycling Programs, 1890-1945. Chicago: Public Works Historical Society, 1979, pp. 1-4.

4 Cal Recovery Systems, Inc. An Evaluation of Processing Methods and Equipment for Use by Multi-Material Recycling Centers. Richmond, CA: March, 1981, p. 1.

5 IBID, p. 2.

6 Oregon Department of Environmental Quality. A Guide to Running a Recycling Project. Portland: May, 1977, p. 3.

7 U.S. Small Business Administration. "Checklist for Going into Business." Small Marketers Aid #71. Washington: September, 1977, p. 4.

8 Darnay, Arsen and William E. Franklin. Salvage Markets for Materials in Solid Waste. Washington: U.S. Environmental Protection Agency, Publication SW-92c, 1972, p. 36.

9 Indiana State Board of Health. A Guide to Recycling the Source Separation Way. Indianapolis: 1979, pp. 5-14.

10 United States Conference of Mayors. Recycling: An Urban Frontier. Washington: Institute for the Development of the Urban Arts and Sciences, December, 1980, p. 10.

11 IBID, pp. 10-12.

12 Indiana State Board of Health. p. 17.

13 IBID, pp. 17-18.

14 Mulligan, Kevin and Jerry Powell. Operating a Recycling Program: A Citizens Guide. Washington U.S. Environmental Protection Agency, Publication SW-770, 1979, pp. 11-13.

178

15 Keep America Beautiful. Recycling: Establishing a Citizen-Sponsored Reclamation Center. p. 3.

16 IBID, p. 4.

17 Cal Recovery Systems, Inc., p. 11.

18 IBID, p. 13.

19 IBID, p. 14.

20 Oregon Department of Environmental Quality. A Guide..., pp. 12-13, 16.

21 Keep America Beautiful, pp. 5-6.

22 Indiana State Board of Health, p. 31.

23 Basic Tools for Recruitment of Volunteers. Chicago: Voluntary Action Center, October 1977, pp. 28-30.

24 IBID, pp. 49-50.

25 Mulligan & Powell, p. 42.

26 Personnel Management. Washington: U.S. Small Business Administration, SBB No. 72, p. 2.

27 Avenoso, Alfred C. How to Set Up a Neighborhood Recycling Center for Environment and Profit. Houston: Houston American Bicentennial Commission, 1975, p. 35.

28 Mulligan & Powell, pp. 54-55.

29 Avenoso, pp. 37-38.

30 "The Whys, Whats, and Whos of Bylaws" in Easier Ways to Organize Groups. Chicago: Citizens Information Service of Illinois, 1980.

31 Not-For-Profit Corporation Guide. Springfield: Illinois Secretary of State, August 1980.

32 Connors, Tracy D. "Tax Consequences for Nonprofit Organizations" in The Nonprofit Organization Handbook. ed. Tracy D. Connors. New York: McGraw-Hill Book Co., 1980, pp. 1-31 to 1-32.

33 Schatz, Willie. "How to Get Nonprofit Status for Your Organization" in Funding Review. July/August 1981, p. 44.

34 Jenkins, Patricia. "Accounting for Nonprofits" in The Grantsmanship Center News. 1977, Issues 20 and 21, reprint, p. 3.

35 IBID, pp. 18-19.

Printed in the United States
17617LVS00002B/120

9 780894 991523